# Modelling
# Hydroelastic
# Vibrations

# Modelling Hydroelastic Vibrations

**Ottó Haszpra**

D. Sc. (Tech.)
Scientific Deputy Director,
Research Centre for Water
Resources Development
(Vituki), Budapest

Pitman

LONDON · BOSTON · MELBOURNE

PITMAN PUBLISHING LIMITED

39 Parker Street, London WC2B 5PB

FEARON PITMAN PUBLISHERS INC.

6 Davis Drive, Belmont, California 94002, USA

*Associated Companies*

Copp Clark Pitman, Toronto
Pitman Publishing New Zealand Ltd, Wellington
Pitman Publishing Pty Ltd, Melbourne

First published 1979
Reprint 1980

Joint edition published by
Pitman Publishing Ltd
and
Akadémiai Kiadó, Budapest

Printed in Hungary

ISBN 0 273 08441 0

# Contents

## V. Model techniques, instrumentation

## VI. Application examples

## VII. Future of hydroelastic modelling

## VIII. References

# Preface

To design hydraulic structures in an economic way entails an exhaustive study of conditions that have hitherto been virtually disregarded. The conditions involve — among others — the phenomena deriving from the dynamic interaction between fluid flow and elastic structure which may give rise to structural vibrations of an inconvenient, harmful or even disastrous nature. These phenomena are usually referred to as hydroelastic ones.

Although research is constantly in progress, no comprehensive work in this field has appeared for a long while. Attention was drawn to this state of affairs by several professionals at the Symposium of the International Association for Hydraulic Research on "Flow-Induced Vibrations of Hydraulic Structures" held in Karlsruhe in 1972, and it thus seemed reasonable to treat the whole topic in the form of a book.

The theory of hydroelasticity,* as well as other sciences, may be helpful to the profession on two levels. It is likely to yield individual solutions for specific design problems, it is likely to create the fundamentals of general procedures enabling the designer to dimension any structure, within certain limitations, with a satisfactory degree of accuracy.

The present state of development of hydroelasticity basically satisfies the requirements of the first level. This means that, based upon hydro-elastic similitude, for a considerable group of hydroelastic phenomena models without difficulties concerning either material or size are to be constructed and data required by the designer are to be checked or determined in them.

As to the second level, it is expected that during the decade to come a theory will be developed on the basis of results of model experiments and

---

* It seems logical to call this branch of science *hydroelastics*, by analogy with mathematics, physics, statics, dynamics, hydraulics, etc., all of which were derived from the Latin (or Greek) in the same way. For example, the Latin "ars dynamica" was first abbreviated to "dynamica" and anglicized to "dynamics". It would be perfectly logical to create the Latin expression "ars elastica" ("Science on elasticity", or more commonly "Strength of materials") and to derive the term "elastica" or in English "elastics". However, the literature does not use this term, — which has quite another meaning — and the author, whose mother-tongue is not English, has no wish to impose his views in this respect.

prototype measurements enabling the solution of most hydroelastic problems to take place directly on the designer's desk.*

Having taken this situation into account as well as the needs of the large-scale hydraulic constructions in progress in Hungary and elsewhere in the world, and viewing finally that results attained in this field in Hungary are new and up-to-date, the author is of the opinion that it would not have been reasonable to wait the five or ten years necessary for writing a comprehensive treatise of the theory of hydroelasticity. It will help the profession very much if the knowledge on the first level, i.e. on the method of hydroelastic similitude and its applications, forming a coherent whole and to be used directly, is published here and now in an independent volume. This book has been written on the basis of such considerations and the author sincerely hopes that he has been able to contribute to satisfying the needs of hydraulic model experimentation and to the development of fluid mechanics. When studying the book, it is an advantage for the reader to have a general knowledge of model experimentation though this is not essential.

The independent researches reported in the book were financially sponsored and morally supported by the Hungarian National Water Authority, the Research Centre for Water Resources Development (VITUKI), Budapest, the Institute for Hydraulic Planning (VIZITERV), Budapest, the Department of Hydraulic Structures of the Budapest Technical University, the Hungarian Institute for Cultural Relations, Budapest, the Ford Foundation, New York, and the Institute of Hydraulic Research of the University of Iowa, Iowa City, Iowa. The major part of the experimental work was carried out in the Hydraulic Laboratory of VITUKI between 1964 and 1972 and in the Iowa Institute of Hydraulic Research in 1968/69.

The author expresses his sincere thanks to the heads and research associates concerned of the above-listed institutions. Illustrations received from the Älvkarleby, the BHRA, the Delft, and the Karlsruhe University hydraulic laboratories have considerably enhanced the pictorial level. He is also indebted to the Hungarian Academy of Sciences for having rendered possible the publication of the book.

*Ottó Haszpra*

---

* The author's optimism seems to have been realistic since, e.g. at the XVIIth IAHR Congress held in Baden-Baden in 1977 (while this book was in the press), strong emphasis was again put on and considerable results were presented concerning generalization in this field [5a, 105c, 148d]. A little earlier, when the book was being proof-read, Kolkman's doctoral thesis [105a] was published summarizing theoretical and experimental results in hydroelastic vibrations.

# List of Symbols

This list contains most of the symbols used throughout the book; other symbols used locally and explained there are not included. The order is alphabetical. Greek letters have been arranged on the basis of their pronunciation; capital letters follow the respective lower case letters. Numerical symbols are to be found at the end of the list.

$a$     assembling alternative where the inertia of the cross section of the cantilever trunk is greater in the direction of flow and smaller in the direction perpendicular thereto

$\alpha$     distortion of the right angle due to shear

$A$     —1. area
2. cross sectional area (e.g. that of a plate, or cable)

$A_k$     area enclosed by the centre line of a pipe wall cross section

$b$     1. plate width
2. other linear dimension
3. assembling alternative where the inertia of the cantilever trunk cross section is smaller in the direction of flow and greater in the direction perpendicular thereto

$c$     1. scale ratio of the linear dimensions (i.e. quotient of corresponding prototype and model lengths)
2. sonic speed
3. distance between the vertical centroidal axis and the vertical centre line

$c_{mb} = \dfrac{m_{pr}}{m_b}$     scale ratio of ballast mass (total prototype mass per ballast mass in model)

$c_{ml} = \dfrac{m_{pr}}{m_l}$     scale ratio of load-bearing mass (total prototype mass to load-bearing mass in model)

$c_X = \dfrac{X_{pr}}{X_m}$     scale ratio of any arbitrary magnitude X, quotient of corresponding prototype and model values

$C$     Chézy's velocity coefficient

$d$     1. basic reference dimension used in the cantilever tests; length of the horizontal edge of the "box"
2. other linear dimension

| | |
|---|---|
| $D = \Delta L / F$ | spring constant of suspension, quotient of the displacement and the force causing it |
| $\Delta$ | double amplitude of the flow-induced vibration of the lower end of the cantilever |
| $\Delta / d$ | relative double amplitude of the flow-induced vibration of the lower end of the cantilever |
| $E$ | 1. Young's modulus in general<br>2. Young's modulus of the structural material |
| $\varepsilon = \dfrac{\Delta L}{L}$ | relative elongation or strain (e.g. that of the suspension cable) |
| $f = \dfrac{10}{T}$ | natural frequency of the lower end of the cantilever in stationary water or air as an average of ten vibrations |
| $f / \sqrt{g/d}$ | relative natural frequency of the lower end of the cantilever in stationary water and air |
| $F$ | force |
| $F_{cap}$ | capillary force due to surface tension |
| $F_{elast}$ | force due to elasticity |
| $F_{grav}$ | force due to gravity |
| $F_{inert}$ | force due to inertia |
| $F_{pres}$ | force due to fluid pressure |
| $F_{str}$ | force due to friction between structural parts |
| $F_{turb}$ | force due to turbulent friction |
| $F_{visc}$ | force due to viscous friction |
| $\Phi$ | angle, angle of torsion over length $L$ |
| $g$ | 1. intensity of the gravity field<br>2. acceleration due to gravity |
| $G$ | 1. shear modulus<br>2. weight<br>3. area weight (weight per surface area of the structural plate) |
| $\gamma$ | 1. specific weight in general<br>2. specific weight of water in particular |
| $\gamma_1$ | specific weight of structural material |

10

| | |
|---|---|
| $h$ | 1. water column (head) |
| | 2. water depth |
| | 3. length of the centreline of a pipe wall cross section |
| $h_d$ | tailwater (downstream) depth |
| $h_d/d$ | relative tailwater depth |
| $h_u$ | headwater (upstream) depth |
| $h_u/d$ | relative headwater depth |
| $H_d$ | tailwater level |
| $I$ | moment of inertia of cross sectional area about an axis |
| $I_p$ | polar moment of inertia of a cross sectional area |
| kp | kilopond (weight of one kilogram mass) = 9.81 newtons |
| $\varkappa$ | universal constant of Kármán |
| l | linear dimension |
| $L$ | linear dimension |
| $L = \ln r$ | logarithmic decrement (logarithm of linear damping) |
| $m$ | 1. mass |
| | 2. as a subscript it refers to a model value |
| $m_b$ | ballast mass in the model |
| $m_l$ | mass of the load-bearing part of the model |
| $M$ | bending moment |
| Mp | megapond (one thousand kiloponds) = 9810 newtons |
| $M_t$ | torsional moment |
| $n$ | 1. frequency of flow-induced vibration of the lower end of the cantilever as an average of ten vibrations (n = 10/T) |
| | 2. number of component plates of the divided plate in the model substituting the prototype plate |
| | 3. as subscript: serial number |
| $n/\sqrt{g/b}$ | relative frequency of the flow-induced vibration of the lower end of the cantilever |
| $N$ | 1. vibration frequency |
| | 2. normal force |
| $\Omega$ | Ohm |
| $\nu$ | kinematic viscosity |

11

| | |
|---|---|
| $p$ | 1. pressure |
| | 2. pond (weight of one gram mass) = 0.00981 newton |
| $q_i$ | 1. momentary double amplitude of the $i$th oscillation of a vibration with linear damping |
| | 2. vertical distance at the $i$th oscillation between the two envelope curves of the oscillogram of an irregular vibration which, on the average, can still be considered as subject to linear damping |
| $Q$ | discharge |
| $r = \dfrac{q_0}{q_1} = \sqrt[10]{\dfrac{q_0}{q_{10}}}$ | measure of linear damping |
| $\varrho$ | 1. density in general |
| | 2. density of water in particular |
| $\varrho_1$ | density of structural material |
| $s$ | plate thickness |
| st | distinctive subscript of data referring to a model with "statically similar elasticity" (data without this subscript relate to models with "dynamically similar elasticity") |
| $S$ | 1. cable force |
| | 2. slope of water surface |
| $t$ | time |
| $T = \displaystyle\sum_{i=1}^{i=10} T_i$ | duration of ten successive vibrations |
| $T_i$ | duration of the $i$th period |
| $v$ | velocity |
| $W$ | load (mass, weight) on unit length (of suspension cable) |
| "0" | that axis of the cantilever trunk cross section about which the moment of inertia is the lowest (it is perpendicular to axis "1") |
| "1" | that axis of the cantilever trunk cross section about which the inertia moment is the highest (it is perpendicular to axis "0") |

# I. Introduction

## 1. On Hydroelasticity in General

The static interaction between a fluid and a rigid body submerged in the fluid or in contact with it is by no means a new topic of *hydraulics*, independent of whether the interaction is really static or dynamic, i.e. the fluid and the rigid body are at relative rest or in relative motion, nevertheless, the pioneering work dealing with the study of structures that undergo deformations due to the dynamic effects of fluid flow and thus react upon the flow itself was performed within the framework of another discipline.

It was a logical consequence of the appearance of the aeroplane and of the rapid development of the aircraft industry that attention was concentrated from many respects on aerodynamic research within the wider field of fluid mechanics. This statement is particularly valid for investigations into the behaviour of elastic bodies submerged in fluid flow since the slender and light aeroplane and rocket structures respond with considerable deformations to the air flow, modifying thus the flow itself.

Studies concerning the flow and vibration phenomena induced by the interaction between the air flow and the elastic body therefore developed into a specific discipline at an early stage. The real development of this branch of *aerodynamics* started after the Second World War and was termed *aeroelasticity* [202].

It was only later that the phenomena accompanying the interactions between the flow and a submerged elastic body, with water as the flowing medium, started to command interest.

Historically speaking, the problem was first met in shipbuilding technology and, prompted by the common features in the relevant investigations, a characteristic discipline referred to since 1958 as *hydroelasticity* [87] was also founded in the domain of hydromechanics.

According to Heller, hydroelasticity deals with phenomena induced by the interaction of inertial, hydrodynamic and elastic forces [87].

Bearing in mind the likely development, primarily the increase in the speed of ships, expected up to 1980, Heller constructed a so-called hydroelastic triangle (Fig. I-1) in which the forces and phenomena constituting the subject of hydroelasticity are presented. This triangle reflects to a considerable extent the viewpoint of the naval architect.

Toebes introduced the concept of *fluidelasticity* [196, 202], which deals with the flow problems (disregarding the quality of the fluid) in which the fluid-dynamic forces mutually depend on the inertial and elastic forces

13

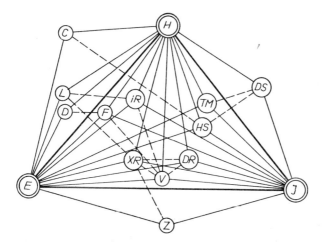

Fig. I-1. Hydroelastic triangle in 1980 according to Heller's forecast [87]. $H$ = hydrodynamic forces, $E$ = elastic forces, $I$ = Inertia forces, $DR$ = dynamic response, $D$ = divergence, $F$ = flutter, $XR$ = explosion response, $L$ = load distribution, $C$ = control effectiveness, $DS$ = dynamic stability, $HS$ = hydroelastic effects on stability, $V$ = mechanical vibration, $Z$ = impact, $IR$ = interference reactions, $TM$ = towing-mooring

induced in the structure. Toebes' fluidelastic triangle (Fig. I-2) reflects mostly the way of thinking of the civil engineer [202].

Naudascher prefers in general the expression *"flow-induced structural vibrations"*, as used in the title of the Karlsruhe Symposium of the International Association for Hydraulic Research (IAHR) arranged in 1972.

The name *hydroelasticity*, introduced nearly two decades ago, is apposite since a characteristic difference between the flow conditions of air and water (the two most frequent media) is caused by the free surface which exists in most cases of water flow and which makes the gravitational effects decisive in the related phenomena. Further differences are due to the insig-

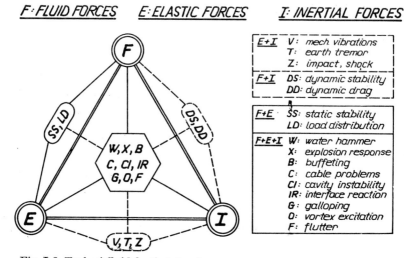

Fig. I-2. Toebes' fluidelastic triangle

14

nificant compressibility and the possibility for cavitation. The difference in order of magnitude of the velocities usually encountered is also significant.

An unquestionable advantage of the term used by Naudascher is that it refers to the main purpose of the investigations, i.e. the determination of the flow-induced *vibrations* of the structure.

Having taken into account the above-mentioned, it is felt that the appropriate definition of hydroelasticity is:

*That science which deals with vibrations of elastic and/or elastically suspended structures arising as a result of the interaction between a flowing medium and the structure.*

Conferences on hydroelasticity generally exclude water hammer phenomena since they deal with problems in which the water itself is considered *incompressible*. This restriction is accepted in this book.

The author's concept of hydroelasticity is that it is a structure-centred science. This is emphasized by the word *vibration* which is generally used for kinds of structural movements satisfying certain criteria [20], while for the periodic movement phenomena belonging to the field of hydraulics the word *vibration* is not applied: oscillation, waving, pulsation, etc. are almost exclusively used.

## 2. Modelling of Hydroelastic Vibrations

Hydroelastic modelling aims to make comprehensible such specified vibration phenomena of an elastic hydraulic structure whose exact mathematical treatment or approximation is, on the present level of the theory of hydroelasticity, neither feasible nor economic. The flow-induced vibration phenomena of hydraulic steel structures composed of plate elements with an intricate geometry belong without doubt to that group therefore their understanding to an acceptable level should be expected only from model experiments (not considering, obviously, measurements carried out on the prototype itself). A reliable model test, however, calls for a knowledge of the criteria of hydroelastic similitude as well as for the exploration of the possibilities for realizing such tests. In this book the method of hydroelastic similitude and its application for modelling will be dealt with.

*Model* in general is taken to be a system (inclusive of the phenomena occurring in it) in a mutually unambiguous relationship with the "prototype" system (inclusive of the phenomena occurring in it) [190] not able to be studied directly for some reason or other. This means that the descriptive equations of the prototype phenomenon and of the modelled one have the same form or can be transformed to such. For example, both the seepage through a porous medium and the passage of an electric current through a conductive material can equally be described by the Laplace differential equation:

$$\varDelta \varphi = \nabla^2 \varphi = \frac{\partial^2 \varphi}{\partial x^2} + \frac{\partial^2 \varphi}{\partial y^2} + \frac{\partial^2 \varphi}{\partial z^2}.$$

It is only the dimension of the terms in the equation that depends on the phenomenon (hydraulic or electric) described. For seepage $\varphi = - kh$, where $k$ (cm/s) is the Darcy coefficient of permeability and $h$ (cm) is the piezometric pressure level in an optional point of the flow field. For electric "flow" $\varphi = - \frac{V}{\varrho}$, where $\varrho$ ($\Omega$cm) is the specific resistance of the conductive medium, and $V$ (Volt) is the electric potential to be measured in an optional point of the conductor. The terms $x$, $y$ and $z$ can designate the coordinates of the general point of the conductive medium, and in this case, they have the interrelationships $X = cx$, $Y = cy$, $Z = cz$ with the coordinates $X$, $Y$, $Z$ of the general point of the porous medium, where the proportionality factor $c$ is the so-called geometrical scale ratio.

Constricting the general formulation, in the following a model will be understood as a replica which from the point of view of the development of the phenomenon, is satisfactorily similar to the prototype. This means that all those elements of the model which influence not negligibly the phenomenon being studied need to be geometrically similar to the adequate element of the prototype. We shall deviate from the geometrical similitude only where it does not influence the similitude of the phenomenon, and on the other hand where eventually it makes possible the realization of the experimental setup at all. (When modelling the flow around a streamlined pier the surface of the pier in contact with the water must obviously be geometrically similar to the corresponding surface of the prototype pier, whereas the wall thickness of the pier, the staircase, the engine room and the engines inside are of no interest. If the pier is not streamlined — e.g. obtuse-ended — smaller deviations in the geometry of the surface in contact with the flow dead zone can be permitted.) Geometrical similarity will only be abandoned for sizes whose exact value does not modify or modifies only marginally the similitude of the phenomena. The phenomena themselves, if necessary, will be distinguished by the attributes "model" or "prototype" or by some other means of recognition. With regard to the characteristics of the phenomenon, it will be required that their dimension should be the same both in the model and the prototype, i.e. the quotients (the so-called "scale ratios") of the corresponding quantities in the prototype and in the model will be dimensionless constants. Because of practical causes it is assumed that the fluid used in the model is the same as that in the prototype, i.e. water. In principle, modelling of hydroelastic vibrations can also be carried out in other ways, nevertheless, for the time being hydroelastic modelling can be considered as being satisfactorily elaborated both generally and in details, with only the above-mentioned restrictions observed.

# II. Antecedents, Beginnings and Basic Problems of Hydroelastic Modelling

## 1. Historical Retrospection

The first hydroelastic model experiment performed in Hungary was in 1958 [55]. Since the most essential parts of this book are based to a great extent on the results obtained in Hungary, the present historical retrospection will mainly — though not exclusively — summarize earlier research results obtained abroad; the more recent results will be utilized in other chapters of the book.

### 1.1 Aeroelastic Model Experiments in Aircraft, Bridge, and Building Construction

As mentioned in the Introduction, hydroelastic research applicable in hydraulic engineering was preceded by the aeroelastic research needed for *aircraft design*. A considerable part of this research, based on various assumptions and fundamental physical relationships, was developed theoretically to enable the computation of the required parameters. Another part of the research work, though also starting from basic physical relationships, utilized the method of model experimentation to seek answers to the questions that arose.

A NATO Manual [94] (undated though probably published in 1959), contains a chapter [177] by the Teddington National Physical Laboratory which summarizes the situation of aircraft modelling at the time. This stated that taking gravity into account would necessitate satisfying the relationship $c_v^2 = c$ (where $c_v$ is the scale ratio of velocity and $c$ is the geometrical scale ratio of the linear dimensions), but since the vibrations caused by air flow are little influenced by gravity this relationship can be ignored. On the other hand, identity of the Mach number cannot be disregarded, i.e. the relationship $c_v = c_c$ must be satisfied, where $c_c$ is the scale ratio for the velocity of sound. The requirement $c_v^2 = c$ is fundamental in most hydraulic experiments while $c_v = c$ has rarely any role. This statement admirably illustrates that in hydroelastic modelling, problems considerably different from those in aeroelasticity must be coped with. The requirements concerning rigidity and mass in aeroelasticity are the same as in hydroelasticity.

In the chapter on modelling [214] of the same manual it is stated that by 1940 there were several countries which had already performed aeroelastic model experiments in attempts to understand flutter phenomena of wings.

18

An analysis of the development attained by 1958 permitted the statement that model experimentation has lost nothing of its significance with the development of computers and it is a competitive or, in many cases, acts as an indispensable partner to the latter. In the author's opinion this statement is still valid and can be extended to hydroelastic model experiments as well.

Aircraft modelling was the first to apply a method according to which the desired rigidity or elasticity of the wings was ensured by incorporating an elastic girder while the wing surface was resolved into several rigid sections connected to each other only by the girder. This method was introduced later [108, 126, 153, 171], apparently independently, in other fields — illustrating the isolation even of sciences not too remote from each other.

*Bridge and building construction* represent another field of application of aeroelasticity, where model experiments were needed in the structural designing of skyscrapers, bridges (mainly suspension bridges), and radio and TV towers. The problems arising in this field are characterized also by the *negligible effect of gravity on vibrations*. While the obvious reason for the development of aeroelastic modelling was the great number of disasters caused not by the pilots but by the weakness of the theoretical fundamentals of design, the disasters caused by aeroelastic effects in bridge and building construction are less familiar. The only exception is, perhaps, the failure in 1940 of the Tacoma Bridge [183], USA in a mild gale by a galloping phenomenon due to the unfortunate cross section of the road structure (Fig. II-1). This was not, however, the first such accident as in 1836 the Brighton Chain Pier in England, in 1854 the Wheeling Bridge over the Ohio River, in 1864 the Queenston Bridge across the Niagara River, in 1889 the Niagara-Clifton Bridge at Niagara Falls all collapsed because of a similar reason. In addition several other bridges required reinforcement and continuous supervision using appropriate instruments (as e.g. the Golden Gate Bridge in San Francisco). Several very tall structures (cooling towers, radar towers) collapsed because of the buffeting phenomenon [201], i.e. because the air vortices separating after passing the towers caused resonant vibrations of one or more other towers.

Fig. II-1. Momentary form of road structure of the Tacoma bridge during the gale resulting in its destruction [202]

It is mentioned here that in Hungary, aeroelastic model studies on bridges were carried out in connection with a number of industrial cable bridges by the Steel Structures Department and Aerodynamics Department of the Budapest Technical University [188].

Because of the *negligibility of gravity effects*, the problems encountered in aeroelastic model investigations of tall buildings are less difficult than those in the case of hydraulic structures. Nevertheless, the author has no information on the application of elastic models, whereas experiments with rigid prisms on spring supports have relatively often been reported [106, 152]. Even so, it seems safe to state that in designing bridges and tall buildings, model studies on the static and dynamic loads of vehicles and mass of people are still more important and more widely used than on the aeroelastic loads, although the solution, with certain approximations, is possible by theoretical calculation. An example is given by Toebes [202] in connection with a monument shaped like an aeroplane wing (Fig. II-2).

### 1.2 Hydroelastic Model Experiments in Naval Architecture

The hull of a vessel negotiating sea waves is generally exposed to flexural effects which may be considered static ones. The model investigation of these effects can be carried out by pressure distribution measurements on *rigid* ship models converted to prototypes by Froude's law, and the deviation from prototype data, according to certain references [108], does not exceed $\pm 1$ per cent. However, the sudden impacts of breaking waves or the impact of the ship's bottom on the water surface results in effects which can be studied only on models complying with Froude's law also from the point of view of structural *elasticity*, since these effects depend essentially on the elasticity of the ship's shell. A particularly dangerous situation occurs if the ship receives impacts in series whose frequency is near to the natural frequency of the hull floating on the water surface.

From Korvin-Kroukovsky's paper [108] it appears that Japanese researchers were the first (in 1951) to attempt modelling the stresses arising in the shell but still based on a hydrostatical concept [171]. The first model experiments in 1954 by the American Lewis [126] and in 1957 by the Japanese Ochi [153] were still performed on models comprising two rigid sections connected by dynamometers. The models used before 1954 were constructed as a single rigid body.

According to Korvin-Kroukovsky, in 1962 no material was known to reproduce the elasticity required in the model. He proposed that the hull be divided into rigid sections joined by waterproof flexible plastic sheets

20

and that the necessary elasticity be reproduced by a suitably designed gird-er according to the scale factor $c_{EI} = c^5$.

This fundamental discovery was correct but even so the realization had an approximative character.

Landweber, in his 1962 manuscript [117] discussing Korvin-Kroukovsky's paper, derived a scale ratio for the cross sectional area of the shell, but as model material, apart from steel, he was only able to recommend bronze and aluminium which are not conducive to satisfactory size reduction.

As stated by Goldrick [48], the only field in naval architecture where the results of *aeroelasticity* can be applied, is the hydroelastic (including: model) investigation of deeply submerged *submarines*. *To ships floating on the surface, the laws of aeroelasticity are inapplicable because of the dominant character of the gravitational force.*

The model studies concerning forces acting on ships made fast in locks, lock bays, and harbours are carried out mostly in the framework of hydraulic engineering since the task in most of these cases is a hydraulically suitable performance of the hydraulic structures and not that of the ships.

### 1.3 Hydroelastic Model Experiments in Hydraulic Engineering

Stollmayer gave a comprehensive survey on the vibrational phenomena in hydraulic structures in 1958 [184]. On model studies there was little to report, the measurements that had been described in literature up till that time, were in general performed on the prototype about which the research institutes and manufacturers concerned published but very few details.

The investigations before 1958 had been performed on structures in closed conduits and apparently according to Froude's law. The models were rigid, their suspensions elastic.

The problem of hydroelastic character concerning the mooring forces during the filling and emptying of navigation locks was in need of solution in many countries of the world as well as in Hungary [57, 169]. [In the experiments that were performed the forces acting on ships in locks during filling and emptying should have been studied. However, since elastic forces are also involved, an exact study could have been done on a hydro-elastic basis, but in some of the investigations the adherence to perfect geometrical similarity and to the same material (steel) resulted in a highly rigid model, while in other cases the effect of the elasticity of the plastic models was disregarded. A similar error was introduced by ignoring the elasticity of the mooring cables (partly because the prototype values were not known). The measuring apparatus applied realized a practically rigid

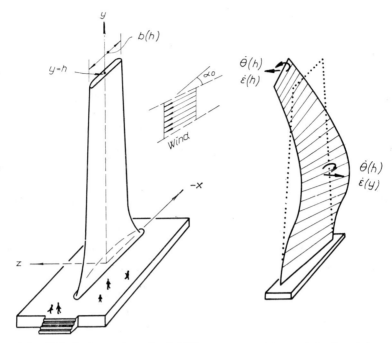

Fig. II-2. Deformation of a foil-like monument in a wind of certain oblique direction indicating momentary direction of deflection velocity $\dot{\varepsilon}$ and angular velocity $\dot{\Theta}$

mooring (Fig. II-3). Consequently, the mooring forces obtained for the prototype must have deviated from the real values to an unknown extent and it can be only supposed that the deviation was on the safe side. Strictly considered, a hydroelastic problem has also to be solved when determining the forces acting on a vessel towed in an inclined tank (Fig. II-4).]

Between 1958 and 1962 Győrke carried out, in the VITUKI laboratory, the first hydroelastic model experiments in Hungary by taking into account the forces of inertia, gravity and elasticity in open-surface flow in accordance with Froude's law, but the lack of adequate materials and instrumentation prevented him from using elastic models and also from developing the relevant theory. His models consisted of *rigid gates suspended* (Fig. II-5) *or supported elastically* [54, 55, 56]. These investigations provided results of great practical importance to the Hydraulic Planning Office **VIZITERV**.

A certain approximation of the hydroelastic behaviour is possible by applying models suspended on weight-tvpe balances. Such a method was used, for example, by Naudascher on tho model of the Duisburg gate [147], and by the author on three models [63, 67] (specified later). Figure **II-6** shows the principle of the measurement. The arrangement details of this

22

Fig. II-3. Study of forces acting on a barge in 1 : 25 scale model of the Nagymaros navigation lock. Forces were measured at two points, in one, and two directions, by strain gauges. Displacement of the model barge did not attain one millimetre (prototype: 2.5 centimetres), i.e. the mooring cable was considerably more "rigid" than one similar to the prototype cable would have been

figure are closest to those applied in the stop-log model of the Nagymaros barrage on the Danube [63, 67]. The principle was the same, the realization (Fig. II-7) a little different from the Duisburg model [147], for which some of the experimental results are illustrated in Fig. II-8.

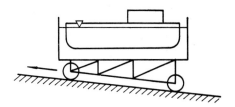

Fig. II-4. Towing a ship in an inclined tank. It is recommended that the elasticity of the mooring be modelled correctly

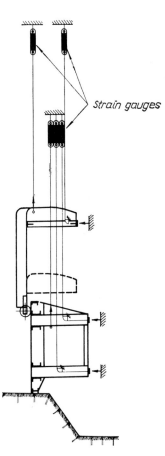

Strain gauges

Fig. II-5. Sketch of force measurements performed on 1 : 25 scale model of first version of the Kisköre Barrage. Strain gauges were inserted into suspension wires whose elasticity (as that of the model in general) corresponded to Froude's law. The model gate structure was of steel and was geometrically similar to the prototype, consequently, it could be considered practically rigid

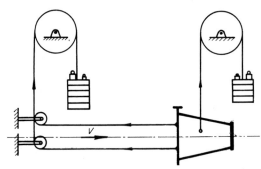

Fig. II-6. Sketch of weight balance system applied to measure lifting force required by the stop-log designed for the Nagymaros Barrage in 1964 [63, 67]. Buffers ensured that for non-equilibrium, the model could not move more than 1 or 2 mm

A similar approximation is supplied by measurement with spring balances. In Fig. II-9 it is shown how the suspension system of a model was adjusted to the measurement range of the spring balance, when the forces to be measured were almost twice as great as the latter. Figure II-10 shows the results of the force measurement (for practical reasons the force is transformed into moment about the pin of the Tainter-gate model) marking the maximum and minimum forces experienced.

Fig. II-7. Essentially that system outlined in Fig. II-6 was applied somewhat earlier by Naudascher for the model of the Duisburg gate (Courtesy Institute of Hydromechanics, Karlsruhe University, FRG.)

The application of either the weight- and the spring-balance methods should, however, be recommended for forces with relatively small oscillation amplitudes only.

An interesting spring-balance supporting a rigid model gate and at the same time being a part thereof was applied by Gál [44] (Fig. II-11).

The newest instrument of VITUKI called "vibromez" which is also suitable for measuring even oscillating forces will be dealt with in detail in Chapter V.

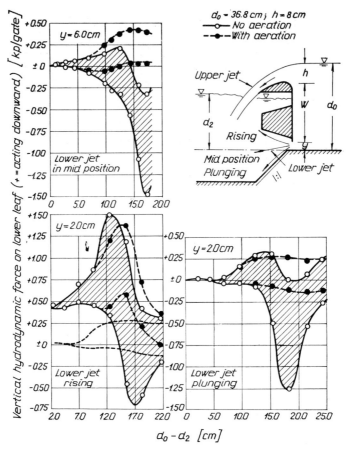

Fig. II-8. Top right: sketch of longitudinal section of the Duisburg model. Top left and at bottom: variation of force acting on lower part of the double Taintor gate

After the few German publications reviewed by Stollmayer and utilized by Győrke, thirty extensive papers on vibrations of hydraulic structures were presented at the VIIIth (Montreal) Congress of the International Association for Hydraulic Research (IAHR) in 1959. These papers showed that a number of model studies had been conducted on the vibrations of hydraulic structures but mainly of those installed in *closed conduits* such as the bottom outlets of high dams. It was at this Congress that Abelev (USSR) presented a paper [2], in which he derived the law of similitude, i.e. the scale ratios, on the basis of different scale model experiments concerning the vibrations of elastically suspended rigid gates (Fig. II-12) in a closed conduit, which rating otherwise corresponds to Froude's law. At the same Congress the Dutchman Kolkman presented a paper [99] on the investiga-

Fig. II-9. Measurement of force components acting on the
pin of the Taintor gate with hinged leaf of the Nagymaros
Barrage

tions related to the Hagestein weir and its *elastic* model (Fig. II-13), as
well as on the theoretical bases of modelling. Both Abelev's and Kolkman's
paper are in agreement with the independently elaborated method expound-
ed in Chapter III, but this latter deals with a wider range of problems
than do the early papers.

Most of the other papers submitted to that Congress did not publish
any modelling principle, but presumably Froude's law was applied with
the elasticity of the suspension being adjusted accordingly. Reynolds' law
is hardly probable because of the need for too high a pressure and discharge.

The year 1959 was the year which brought the disaster that prompted
the more extensive application of hydroelastic model experiments. According

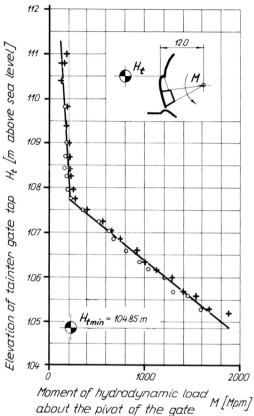

Fig. II-10. Measurement results of required lifting force of Nagymaros Taintor gate without its own weight, on the basis of spring scale measurement, indicating the maximum and minimum forces experienced, converted to the prototype. (Geometrical centre of Taintor gate arch is 1 m above pin.)

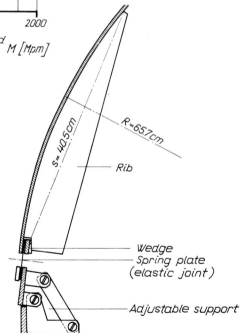

Fig. II-11. Substitution of elastic suspension of a hinged-leaf gate by an elastic cantilever-like clamping of the hinged-leaf

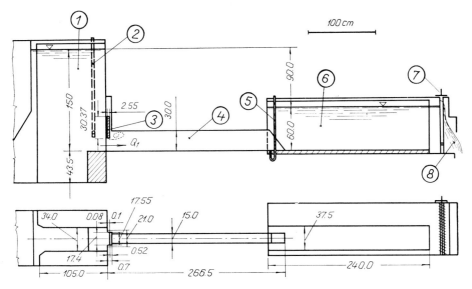

Fig. II-12. Abelev's "1 : 1" model. Plan and longitudinal section of experimental setup. 1 — pressure tank, 2 — gauge pipe, 3 — gate, 4 — pipe line, 5 — piezometric pipe, 6 — tailwater flume, 7 — tailwater level regulator, 8 — outflow

Fig. II-13. Visor gate at Hagestein (Courtesy Delft Hydraulics Laboratory, The Netherlands)

to the report of Uppal [208], the suspension of a gate in the diversion tunnel of the Bhakra dam under construction broke during a flood because of violent flow-induced vibrations. The gate shaft also collapsed and the power station was inundated. Because of the damage, construction work was interrupted for several months.

Mention must also be made of Campbell's 1961 paper [24] according to which two gate structures were studied in models after 1947; these were reproduced by rigid masses on elastic suspensions. Since Campbell quotes results in good agreement with prototype measurements, it is highly likely that the modelling was based on Froude's law. The original report [182] was not available but it appears that in closed conduits these investigations were the world's first hydroelastic model studies concerning hydraulic structures.

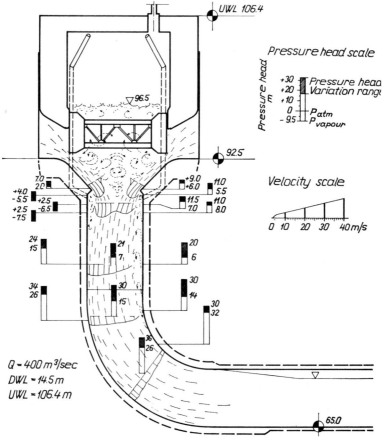

Fig. II-14. Pressure oscillations in inlet shaft diversion tunnel. In similar cases it is recommended to check whether or not hydroelastic vibrations occur

Since the Montreal Congress a great number of papers have been published on hydroelastic problems. Among the congress papers themselves and among other papers there are many references to model studies without any data on the models. Some papers give certain data of the model but not the similitude principles. A somewhat more detailed modelling theory has appeared but in a few papers only. Save a few exceptions, a similar scarcity obtains in the case of model techniques and instrumentation. The most significant papers will be quoted later on in the respective chapters, nevertheless, some outstanding model investigations should be mentioned.

A paper by Angelin [11] from 1959 reported on an interesting hydroelastic experiment concerning a duplex gate and the shaft of a diversion tunnel, where considerable pressure oscillations were observed (Fig. II-13). According to the paper no inclination to vibrate was experienced, nevertheless, we must add that in similar situations the danger of hydroelastic vibrations is very high and it is therefore recommended that very careful model studies be carried out prior to the realization in prototype.

Angelin and Flagestad [12] presented the results of an experiment series concerning the behaviour of semicircular (arched) stop-logs during lowering

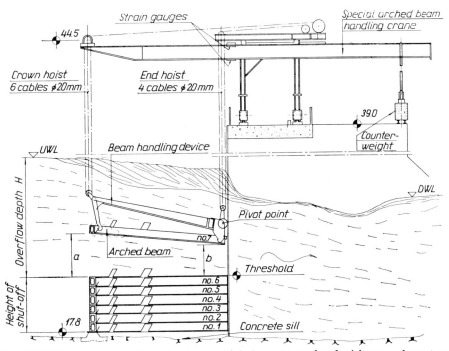

Fig. II-15. Lowering of arched stop-logs at high downstream level with some characteristic dimensions

31

Fig. II-16. 1 : 15 scale model of the arched stop-log closure in function (Courtesy Hydraulic Laboratory, Älvkarleby, Sweden)

in flowing water, this being a typical hydroelastic problem. The prototype arrangement, together with a few informative geometrical data, are presented in Fig. II-15. The model (scale 1 : 15) in operation is shown in Fig. II-16, with a more or less similar prototype operation being shown in Fig. II-17. As can be seen, the arched stop-logs were lowered (and lifted) by a special $T$-shaped handling device and both the stop-log and the handling device were attacked by hydrodynamic forces. Since the state of flow was highly three-dimensional, it is evident that by no theoretical method could the problem have been tackled reliably. Prototype measurements have shown a fair agreement with model data. The hydrodynamic load on the beam and the amplitude of its variation was in good agreement with Froude's law. As for the frequencies, the prototype values proved to be 20 to 30 per cent higher than in the 1 : 15 model. The paper does not expressly

Fig. II-17. Prototype situation similar to that in Fig. II-16 (Courtesy Hydraulic Laboratory, Älvkarleby, Sweden)

state whether or not the elasticity of the beams followed Froude's law or whether only the suspension was elastically similar. It seems that the model beams were practically rigid. In the author's opinion, in similar situations where the steel structures are relatively slender, it is necessary to model not only the form and the mass distribution of the beams but also their elasticity according to Froude's law.

Harrison's paper [60] presented at the Leningrad Congress of the IAHR treats the model tests of a siphon spillway. The tests were aimed at determining the pressure and vibration conditions of the hood of the siphon. Dimensioning of the 1 : 12 scale model followed Froude's law, including the elasticity and mass distribution of the hood, whereas other parts of the structures were considered and modelled as being practically rigid. The necessary elasticity of the model hood was attained by applying a nylon-

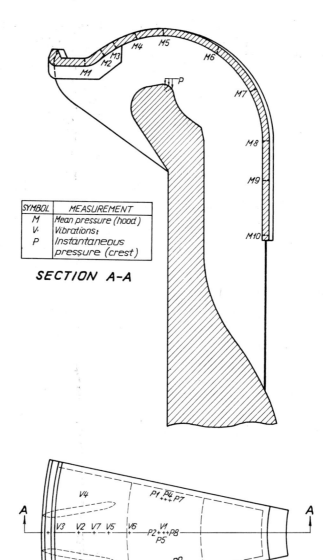

| SYMBOL | MEASUREMENT |
|--------|-------------|
| M | Mean pressure (hood) |
| V. | Vibrations; |
| P | Instantaneous pressure (crest) |

SECTION A-A

PLAN

Fig. II-18. Cross section of elastic siphon model with locations of measurement points

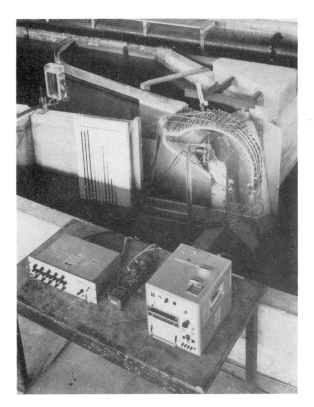

Fig. II-19. Siphon model (Courtesy Hydraulic Research Station, Wallingford, England)

reinforced resin and a slight modification of the thickness. The cross section and plan of the structure with the measurement points is given in Fig. II-18; a photo of the model is shown in Fig. II-19. The latter illustration indicates the brass weights glued to the hood to adjust the mass to the correctly scaled value.

Lean reported in Leningrad about the model investigation of a temporary coffer dam wall [122]. It was intended to use this wall as an enclosure of the building site during the construction of a power house in the Mangla dam project. It had to withstand the pressures in the vortex flow surrounding the jets from four tunnels when delivering the flood flow of the river. Figure II-20 illustrates the situation with some characteristic dimensions, Fig. II-21 shows the 1 : 50 scale model. In the upper part of the picture, the temporary wall can be seen which in the prototype consists of a series of horizontal I-beams faced with timber boarding, the boarding being

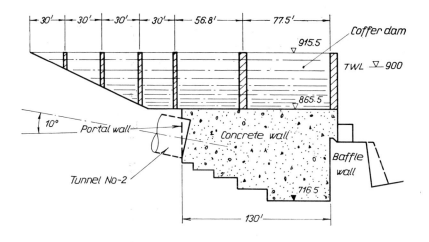

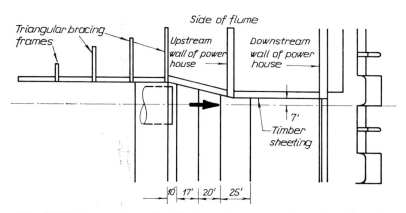

Fig. II-20. Arrangement of coffer dam of power station and outlet of one tunnel with some characteristic dimensions

bolted to the beams. For the sake of elastic similarity the model of this wall was realized by using a rigid PVC sheet with brass weights added, to achieve the similarity of mass distribution, too. On the basis of the measurements, vibration amplitudes and frequencies of several points of the wall were analysed.

Coxon, Angelin and Wardle reported about the model and prototype investigation of the stop-log closure of the Kainji dam, Nigeria [26a, 186b]. Figure II-22 shows the lowering operation of the concrete stop-log by means of the handling beam in the prototype; Fig. II-23 presents some of the model test results, converted into prototype values, concerning the vertical hydrodynamic loads on the two-component unit. During the course of

36

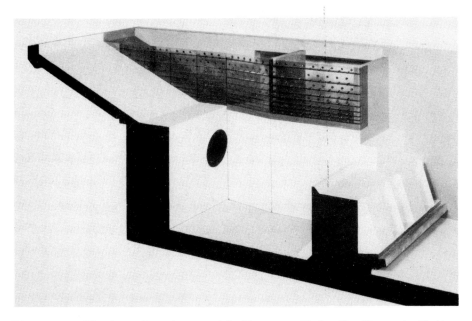

Fig. II-21. Elastic coffer dam model (Courtesy Hydraulic Research Station, Wallingford, England)

these experiments only the suspension was considered elastic; the beams were assumed to be rigid — this assumption being acceptable since the concrete beam is made very rigid because of the large one-sided hydrostatic force it has to withstand. The results from the model and the prototype were in good agreement with each other apart from one event of severe overloading of the seventh prototype stop-log which could not be reproduced subsequently in the model despite repeated tests. One may suppose that some hydraulic event with a very low probability or some mechanical disturbance occurred. Just the same, it calls attention to the need for very thorough carrying out of the model tests particularly concerning small details of the structures which are in contact with flowing water (seals, edges, etc.). In Naudascher's opinion [148b] the difficulties with modelling the flow through very narrow openings resulted in conclusions not valid for the prototype.

At the XVIIth IAHR Congress (Baden-Baden, 1977), a number of papers on hydroelastic model experiments were presented, e.g. [5a, 37a, 97b, 105b] which are worthy of study.

Fig. II-22. Lowering a concrete stop-log at the Kainji Dam (Courtesy Hydraulic Laboratory, Älvkarleby, Sweden)

## 2. General Remarks on Similitude

The engineer performs the design of structures by means of relationships derived for an actual case from a few fundamental laws of mechanics. This statement is valid in the mechanics of both solids and fluids. These fundamental laws describe the static or dynamic (kinetic) equilibrium of elementary particles of bodies by means of relationships between stresses, deformations and changes in velocity. By taking another step backward: the theory of strength of elastic materials is based on Hooke's generalized law [22]. The laws of motion of accelerating bodies also involve Newton's second law [22]. The basic laws of fluid motion are, according to the nature of flow, either the Navier–Stokes or the Reynolds sets of differential equations [151]. This, however, means nothing other than that by maintaining

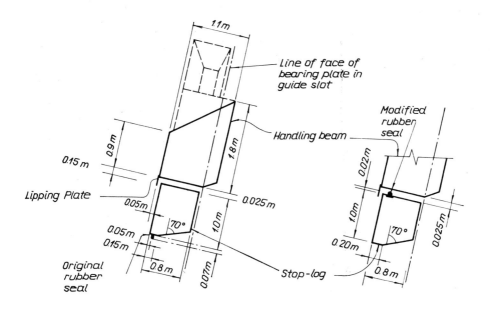

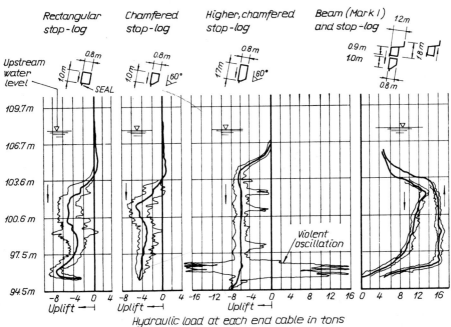

Note: Zero load = stop-log or handling beam or both hanging freely in air

Fig. II-23. Top: Cross section of stop-log and handling beam with original and the modified rubber seal. Bottom: measurement results concerning lowering and lifting forces without own weight

Newton's second law, Hooke's law becomes replaced by relationships concerning the elastic compression and the laminar or turbulent friction of the fluid. In the case of free fluid surfaces the law of surface tension [151], too, belongs to the fundamental laws to be observed.

When recalling the above-listed laws of nature, we followed the historical order of the development of science. We must state, however, that all these laws of nature can be formulated in the framework of the transport theory [192] which was developed in the second quarter of this century and which eloquently expresses the unity of nature. The general transport equation which involves all of those laws of nature is

$$\frac{\partial \varrho_i}{\partial t} + \operatorname{div} \bar{j}_i = q_i .$$

In this equation $\varrho_i$ is the density of the so-called $i$th extensive magnitude, characterizing the phenomenon, $t$ is the time, $\bar{j}_i$ is the flow density of the $i$th extensive magnitude, and $q_i$ is the source density of the $i$th extensive, magnitude in an optional point. The flow density itself is

$$\bar{j}_i = \varrho_i \bar{v} + \sum_{k=1}^{n} L_{ik} \operatorname{grad} y_k$$

in which $\bar{v}$ is the velocity of the medium transporting the extensive properties through an optional point of the space (and, therefore, $\varrho_i \bar{v}$ is the convective flow density), $y_k$ is the so-called $k$th intensive magnitude characterizing the phenomenon, and $L_{ik}$ is the conductivity factor (i.e. the flow density of the $i$th extensive magnitude in the case of unit gradient of the $k$th intensive magnitude). It means that the product $L_{ik} \operatorname{grad} y_k$ is the conductive flow density.

The general transport equation, when applied in the field of hydromechanics and strength of materials, can be used to express the momentum transport and the sourceless energy and mass transport. In the special investigations to be treated in the framework of this book the transport theory will not be utilized but in the future it can be expected that its application will result in considerable progress in the field of hydromechanics and within this in that of hydroelasticity.

When facing a specific problem, its solution is often based on some relationship open to direct perception, or for the sake of a feasible solution, some approximations or simplifications are assumed. This by no means influences the validity of the fundamental laws (laws of nature). The information content of any equation for the concrete case and that of the fundamental laws completed with the conditions of solution (boundary conditions, etc.) must be the same, within the permitted margin of error.

This latter statement is very important from the viewpoint of the practical establishment of similitude criteria. Namely, two phenomena are similar to their mathematical models, i.e. the equations describing the phenomenon together with the respective conditions of solution (involving the initial and boundary conditions as well as specification of the domain of validity), are to be brought to the same form [190]. In this case, the two phenomena may be regarded as models of each other.

Since a concrete phenomenon among conditions given, may contain, from the fundamental laws to the eventual concrete final equation very many descriptive equations all of which contain exactly the same amount of information, this is obviously very helpful in finding another phenomenon similar to the one to be studied, and/or in determining the criteria of similitude.

Obviously, if it is possible to derive final equations suitable for practical use from the fundamental laws, these equations should be applied in planning and design, and model experiments are no longer needed. If, however, anywhere in the course of derivation from the fundamental laws, some mathematical difficulty arises (usually owing to the complexity of the mathematical formulation of the conditions of solution) or if the actual application of the derived equations would be too time-consuming (e.g. if there is no computer program and it would be too expensive to develop one, or if the computation itself requires too much computer time), the solution, or a cheaper solution, may be offered by the model experiment. A sketch of the solution procedure is given in Fig. II-24, where the alternative character of the computation and the model experiment methods is pointed out.

It is expedient to derive the conditions of similitude from the fundamental laws (laws of nature) since those do not contain any approximation. Very often, however, one (or some) of the derived equations may be utilized instead, due to its simplicity, or to the easier handling of secondary variables introduced (e.g. moment of inertia instead of direct geometrical sizes, etc.). In this book too, the conditions of similitude will be derived either from the fundamental laws or from equations obtained from these laws through more or less circuitous procedures. On the basis of the similitude conditions deduced the model can be designed and constructed and — follow-

Fig. II-24. Steps in solving a design problem

ing the measurement–experimental plan outlined earlier — the model experiment can be carried out.

The model experiment yields the actual values of the quantities relevant for the user by means of direct measurement and then multiplication by the constant scale ratio. A disadvantage of the model experiment is that the special law dominating the variation of these quantities either escapes any formulation or is available only as an empirical equation not reflecting the connection to the fundamental laws. Thus, the model is a "black box" from which, if the fundamental laws and the scaled conditions of solution are put in, the equally scaled results may be obtained as the output in the form of numerical values or distributions. However, the essential thing to be emphasized is that the needs of practice are thus generally satisfied, especially in cases where the unsatisfactory state of development of the mathematical apparatus would not permit one to attain even such numerical solutions. Naturally, every effort should be made to solve design problems by computation. The computation may prove more advantageous even if its cost is of the same order of magnitude as that of the model experiment, since, in general, model experiments are more time-consuming than the use of a computer; even though the program may be complicated but already available. Nevertheless, taking care of the further development of modelling is necessary not only because in this way the sphere of problems solvable economically in models is to be enlarged but also because the model test results may contribute to the development or checking of new computation methods.

In this book the fundamental questions of modelling and similitude will not be treated since in this respect a wide selection of works in several languages is at the reader's disposal (among them we recall first of all the work of E. Szűcs [190]). We shall concentrate our attention exclusively on the modelling of vibrations of elastic hydraulic structures.

### 3. Modelling of Hydraulic Structures in General

The modelling of flow phenomena developing around hydraulic structures incapable of motion, including vibrations, may be considered as satisfactorily solved [61, 93]. In the case of a free-surface turbulent flow the similitude is determined by Froude's law. In the case of flow in a closed conduit, similitude is based, depending on other circumstances, upon the Euler, the Reynolds, or again the Froude model law [8, 51, 61, 151, 215].*

* As is well known, the Froude model law prescribes the identity of the Froude number (invariant) in the homologous points of the prototype and the geometrically similar model. That is, $v^2/gl =$ idem, where $v$ is the velocity, $g$ is the intensity of the

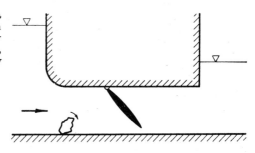

Fig. II-25. Movement of a model of a tilting gate or of a rolling stone can be studied with satisfactory accuracy only on the basis of Froude's law, even in a closed-conduit turbulent flow

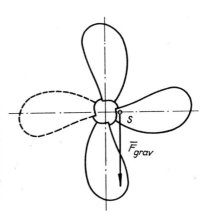

Fig. II-26. Movement of a non-vertical-axis tubular turbine or a submarine or ship screw, with one of the blades broken, may be studied by applying Froude's law, though if all the blades are unharmed, an exact modelling is to be carried out only on the basis of Reynolds model law. (Approximately, the Euler or Froude's law is acceptable, too.) $S$ = centre of gravity, $F_{grav}$ = weight force of turbine after breaking

The model laws mentioned consider properly only the forces acting on the fluid particles and on the surface of solid bodies, when the tensions arising inside solid bodies do not modify the flow at all, because of the infinite or very high rigidity of the structure. However, the validity of these laws must be studied profoundly for such model investigations where the solid body can move and its movement is influenced by any force disregarded, when deriving the afore-mentioned model laws. Thus, for

gravitational field and $l$ is a characteristic length. This law is valid if forces dominating the flow phenomenon are the inertia and the gravitational forces in both the prototype and the model.

The Reynolds model law prescribes the identity of the Reynolds number, that is, $vl/v$ = idem, where $v$ is the kinematic viscosity of the fluid. This law is valid if the dominating forces are those of inertia and viscous friction.

The Euler model law prescribes the identity of the Euler number, that is, $v^2\varrho/\Delta p$ = idem, where $\varrho$ is the density of the fluid and $\Delta p$ is the pressure difference between two characteristic points. This law is valid if the dominating forces are those of inertia and hydrodynamic pressure. (This law follows from Froude's law but not conversely.)

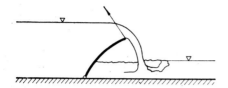

Fig. II-27. In open surface flow, elasticity of suspension (and possibly that of the gate) must follow Froude's law

example, without dwelling upon details, the application of the Froude's law does not constitute any difficulty when studying the movement of such rigid bodies put into turbulent flow whose specific gravity is arbitrary and whose connection (shaft, ball-and-socket joint, inextensible filament, friction at rest or even no mechanical connection at all) to the boundary wall is not elastic. A few examples are shown in Figs II-25 and II-26. If the connection of the rigid body to the wall is such that the dimension of its displacement depends on the force arising in the connecting element (elastic suspension, sliding support with some kind of friction), modelling is possible only if these forces are to be adjusted to Froude's law (Figs

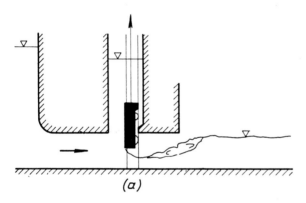

(a)

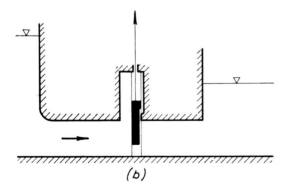

(b)

Fig. II-28. In a closed tunnel with an open-surface shaft (a), Froude's law is compulsory in studying the movements of the gate. In pressure chamber (b), movement of the gate may be modelled quite accurately according to Reynolds' law, though the Froude or Euler type modelling may also prove more or less satisfactory. Elasticity and structural friction of suspension (and possibly those of the gate) have to satisfy the same laws

II-27, II-29). The same holds for deformable bodies in which stresses depending on the deformation arise, etc. The modelling of problems of this type was long considered impossible, nevertheless, it has not proved to be hopeless to search for a method that satisfies the model law valid for the flow and followed absolutely with respect to the structure, too, with an adequate degree of accuracy.

# III. Hydroelastic Similitude

In this chapter, which forms the backbone of the book, the force effects to be considered in the theory of hydroelasticity, the possibilities of modelling them or ignoring them, furthermore, assuming the more or less general and special cases, the scale ratios between the corresponding quantities in the model and the prototype will be treated in detail.

The results of the hydroelastic similitude method, to be treated according to the above system, will be valid for modelling the vibrations of hydraulic structures made of arbitrary solid, nonplastic (i.e. perfectly elastic) materials. Nevertheless, as demonstrated by experimental evidence, they can also be used satisfactorily for structures with finite internal damping. Hydraulic structures, in most cases, are composed of concrete or steel. The general statements of this chapter are valid for both types. Since, however, vibration problems have rarely been experienced with the practically rigid concrete structures of great inertia, in elaborating certain details, the solution of the special problems of steel structures — in particular those of the gate-like structures composed of plate elements — were aimed at first of all.

As mentioned in Section II. 2, the similitude criteria can be determined both from the fundamental laws dominating the particular sphere of phenomena and from any of the equations derived. Since fundamental laws contain the fewest simplifications and omissions we shall therefore strive to support ourselves directly on the fundamental laws. We shall start from a derived equation only if the application of the fundamental law is too complicated or the result obtained therefrom would only be applicable with difficulty.

The hydroelastically similar models mean only a further development of the hydraulically (and hence also geometrically) similar models, therefore the geometric and kinematic similarity will be maintained, i.e. the geometrical scale ratio $c$ (the quotient of the prototype length $L_{pr}$ and the corresponding model length $L_m$), furthermore the kinematic scale ratio $c_t$ (the quotient of the prototype time $t_{pr}$ and the corresponding model time $t_m$) must be constant independently of time, location and any other factor:

$$c = L_{pr}/L_m = \text{const.} \tag{0a}$$

$$c_t = t_{pr}/t_m = \text{const.} \tag{0b}$$

The dynamic similarity is based on the fundamental laws (force laws) of mechanics. This will be treated in detail since a deviation from hydraulically similar models in the customary sense appears in this respect.

## 1. Forces Influencing the Movement of Hydraulic Structures and their Scale Ratios in General

Let us look at the fundamental force laws that influence the movement of an elastic body put into the flow and the motion of the fluid itself. For the sake of simplicity and expediency, fluid will be understood to be water and air since all the structures we are concerned with in practice are in contact only with those, and the same is virtually true in the laboratory, too.

The flow and the structure, according to the static concept of d'Alembert, are under the effect of the following forces (indicating in parentheses whether or not they are dominant in the sphere of the phenomena* studied):

1. *Force of inertia*, $F_{inert}$. (It is significant for water and for the movable parts of the structure, whereas so far as air is concerned, it is generally not significant.)

2. *Field force*, in the particular case exclusively the *gravity force*, $F_{grav}$. (It is significant first of all as, for example, the cause of the hydrostatic pressure, for water and sometimes for the structure, while in the air and mostly also in the structure, it produces only a background stress which does not influence the movements.)

3. *Elastic force*, $F_{elast}$. (For water and air, with the exception of air closures, its effect is negligible, while for the structure it is significant.)

4. *Turbulent friction*, $F_{turb}$. (This acts on the interfaces between water and water, or water and air layers, and on the wetted surfaces of the bed and the submerged parts of the structures. Depending on the circumstances, its effect on the water may be significant but on the air, in the sphere of the phenomena studied, it is completely negligible.)

5. *Viscous friction*, $F_{visc}$. (It may occur in water and in air, as well as on the surface of the structure. Nevertheless, in most cases it is negligible in comparison with turbulent friction, and is nearly always negligible in air.)

* It is emphasized that exclusively the phenomena concerning *hydraulics* are concerned. Therefore, though also hydraulic structures may be in contact with air as, e.g. in the case of a partially submerged gate, the effect of air in general can be neglected without any rigorous study. In aerodynamics it is precisely the friction and inertia of the air which dominate while water, in most cases, is absent.

6. *Hydrodynamic fluid pressure*, $F_{pres}$. (Significant in water, generally insignificant in air.)

7. *Friction between structural parts*, $F_{str}$. (It arises, for example, at nodes, bearings, seals, etc. In many cases it can be neglected, in others not. According to character, it can be linear or follow the Coulomb law.)

8. *Capillary force*, $F_{cap}$. (It is equally negligible for water, air and the structure.)

Without the need for proof, it can be stated that allowance should generally be made for the effects of inertial force, gravity, fluid pressure, and elastic force, while those of viscous and turbulent fluid friction and of structural friction must be investigated separately. Capillarity need not be dealt with.

From the literature on hydromechanics [61, 151, 216] the scale ratios of the forces listed are well-known.*

For the sake of completeness, hereunder they will be derived briefly as follows:

1. *Force of inertia* (D'Alembert's reaction to any accelerating force, independently of whether it affects water, air or solid bodies):

$$F_{inert} = -ma$$

in which $m$ is mass, $a$ is acceleration (Fig. III-1).

Its scale factor

$$c_{F\,inert} = \frac{-m_{pr}\,a_{pr}}{-m_m\,a_m} = \frac{\varrho_{pr}\,V_{pr}\,a_{pr}}{\varrho_m\,V_m\,a_m} = c_\varrho\,c^3\,c\,c_t^{-2} = c_\varrho\,c^4\,c_t^{-2} = c_\varrho\,c^2\,c_v^2 \qquad (I)$$

in which $V$ is volume, $\varrho$ is density. The subscript pr refers to prototype, the subscript m refers to the model, $c$ is the geometrical scale ratio, $c_\varrho$, $c_t$ and $c_v$ are the scale ratios of density, time and velocity, respectively.

2. *Gravity force*

$$F_{grav} = mg$$

---

* According to the modern approach [19, 190, 192] similitude criteria and the individual scale ratios can be derived on the basis of the equations describing the momentum transport and the sourceless energy and mass transport. In the literature referred to in the text [61, 151, 215], restricted to this particular sphere of hydromechanic problems (otherwise perfectly rightly) the expressions (describing equations, mathematical models of the phenomenon) of the forces dominating the phenomena are written directly and due to the wish that the ratio of prototype forces and the corresponding forces in the model, satisfying geometrical and kinematical similarity, should be constant, the scale ratios listed in equations I–VI are derived.

in which $g$ is the intensity of the gravitational field whose value is equal to that of the acceleration due to gravity (Fig. III-2).

$$c_{F\,grav} = \frac{m_{pr}\,g_{pr}}{m_m\,g_m} = \frac{\varrho_{pr}\,V_{pr}\,g_{pr}}{\varrho_m\,V_m\,g_m} = c_\varrho\,c^3\,c_g \qquad\qquad \text{(II)}$$

in which $c_g$ is the scale ratio of the gravitational force (usually its value is 1).

3. *Force due to elasticity*

(a) *in fluids:*

$$F_{elast} = E_0\,A\,\frac{\varDelta V}{V}$$

in which $E_0$ is the volumetric Young's modulus of water, $\varDelta V$ is the change of the volume $V$, $A$ is an area on the boundary or inside of the $V$ volume which is attacked by a force $F_{0\,elast}$ (Fig. III-3). The scale ratio of this last one:

$$c_{F_0\,elast} = c_{E_0}\,c^2$$

in which $c_{E_0}$ is the scale ratio of the volumetric Young's modulus of water or air.

(b) *in solid bodies:*

$$F_{elast} = EA\,\frac{\varDelta L}{L}$$

in which $E$ is Young's modulus of the structural material, $A$ is a cross

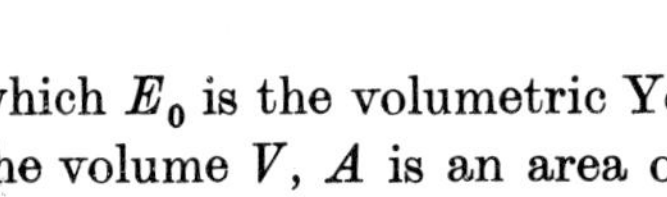

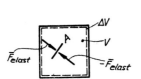

Fig. III-1. Active force $\overline{F}_{act}$ resulting in acceleration $\overline{a}$ of mass $m$ and the d'Alembert reaction $\overline{F}_{inert}$

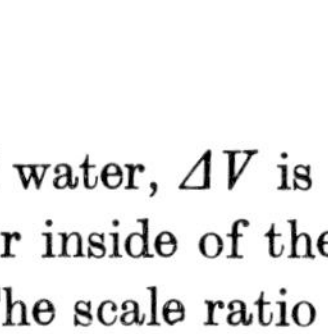

Fig. III-2. Gravitational force acting on mass $m$

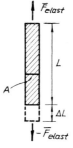

Fig. III-3. Elastic force $\overline{F}_{elast}$ acting on a surface $A$ in fluid body when fluid volume $V$ is compressed by $\varDelta V$

Fig. III-4. Elastic force $\overline{F}_{elast}$ causing an elongation $\varDelta L$ of original length $L$ of a solid bar

sectional area attacked by the force $F_{\text{elast}}$, $\Delta L$ is the change of length $L$ due to $F_{\text{elast}}$ (Fig. III—4). The scale ratio for the elastic force

$$c_{F\text{ elast}} = c_E\, c^2$$

in which $c_E$ is the scale ratio of Young's modulus of the structural material.

Consequently, the scale ratio of the elastic forces in general can be written as

$$c_{F\text{ elast}} = c_E\, c^2 \qquad\qquad\qquad (\text{III})$$

in which now $c_E$ denotes the scale ratio of both the volumetric or the linear Young's modulus.

4. *Turbulent wall friction* can be obtained from the relationship between the slope-directed component of the gravity force and the Chézy formula ($v = C\sqrt{RS}$) for open channel flow (Fig. III-5):

$$F_{\text{turb}} = A_\gamma RS = A\varrho g\, \frac{v^2}{C^2}$$

in which $R$ is the hydraulic radius, $S$ is the surface slope.

The scale ratio of the turbulent wall friction:

$$c_{F\text{ turb}} = c^2 c_\varrho\, c_g\, \frac{c_v^2}{c_C^2} = c^2 c_v^2\, c_\varrho\, c_g\, c_C^{-2} \qquad\qquad (\text{IVa})$$

in which $c_C$ is the scale ratio of Chézy's velocity coefficient.

This deduction is based on special equations derived for water movement but it is very useful because it contains the velocity coefficient actually used in practice. If the fundamental law of turbulent flow is applied, a similar result is obtained which, however, does not contain Chézy's $C$, and which, as will be demonstrated later, is not in contradiction with equation (IVa). As a fundamental law, the equation for the turbulent friction [51] can be used, according to which (by disregarding the sign):

$$\tau_{yx} = \varrho\, \overline{v_x'\, v_y'}$$

in which $\tau_{yx}$ is the shear stress in the $x$ direction of the plane whose normal

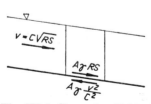

Fig. III-5. Channel wall friction of free surface flow

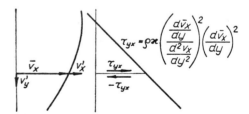

Fig. III-6. Velocity and shear stress distributions in turbulent flow

is $y$, $v'_x$ and $v'_y$ are the pulsation components of the velocity in the direction of the subscript-indicated axes (Fig. III-6). The pulsation components are given as products of the mixing length $l$ and the derivative (gradient) in the $y$ direction of the average velocity component in the $x$ direction $\bar{v}_x$. If the mixing length is expressed according to Kármán's universal assumption — according to which the mixing length is linearly proportional to the above-mentioned first derivative of the velocity and inversely proportional with its second derivative taken in the same direction — the equation for the shear stress will be

$$\tau = \varrho \varkappa^2 \left( \frac{\dfrac{d\bar{v}_x}{dy}}{\dfrac{d^2\bar{v}_x}{dy^2}} \right)^2 \left( \frac{d\bar{v}_x}{dy} \right)^2$$

in which $\varkappa = 0.4$ is Kármán's universal constant. From this, through multiplication by the elementary surface $dA_y = dx\,dz$, the turbulent friction force acting on the elementary surface will be

$$dF_{\text{turb}} = dF_y\, \varrho \varkappa^2 \left( \frac{\dfrac{d\bar{v}_x}{dy}}{\dfrac{d^2\bar{v}_x}{dy^2}} \right)^2 \left( \frac{d\bar{v}_x}{dy} \right)^2,$$

while the relationship between the scale ratios:

$$c_{F_{\text{turb}}} = c^2\, c_\varrho\, c^2\, c_v^2\, c^{-2} = c^2\, c_v^2\, c_\varrho. \tag{IVb}$$

This relationship, being generally valid for low-viscosity fluids, is valid for both water and air.

5. *The viscous friction force* (for water and air):

$$F_{\text{visc}} = A\eta \frac{dv}{dn} = A\nu\varrho \frac{dv}{dn}$$

in which $\eta$ is the dynamic viscosity, $\nu$ is the kinematic viscosity, and $dv/dn$ is the rate of variation of velocity in the direction perpendicular to both the friction plane and the velocity (or velocity component) (Fig. III-7).

The scale ratio of the viscous friction force:

$$c_{F_{\text{visc}}} = c^2\, c_\nu\, c_\varrho\, c_v\, c^{-1} = c\, c_v\, c_\nu\, c_\varrho \tag{V}$$

in which $c_\nu$ is the scale ratio of the kinematic viscosity.

6. *The hydrodynamic pressure force* (for water and air):

$$F_{\text{pres}} = pA$$

in which $p$ is the hydrodynamic pressure and $A$ is the area acted upon. The scale ratio of the hydrodynamic pressure force:

$$c_{F_{\text{pres}}} = c_p c^2. \tag{VI}$$

It can easily be demonstrated that $c_{F_{\text{pres}}} = c_{F_{\text{inert}}}$ since the hydrodynamic pressure force derives from the inertia of the fluid.

The next section will refer to scale ratios of forces that are necessarily or possibly identical.

7. The types of *structural friction*

(a) *Friction at rest* appears at the interface of structural parts if a relative displacement is kinematically possible but is not induced by streamflow effects.

This situation is equivalent to the one where the structure is materially coherent along these interfaces. The limit value (potential maximum) of the structural friction force at rest is

$$F_{\text{str}, r} = \mu_r N$$

in which $\mu_r$ is the friction coefficient at rest and $N$ is the normal force (Fig. III-8).

The scale ratio for friction at rest is

$$c_{F_{\text{str}, r}} = c_{\mu_r} c_N. \tag{VIIa}$$

(b) *Constant (Coulomb) friction* arises on surfaces (or surface parts) along which friction is independent of the slip velocity. Dry friction for example, is of such type. The relationship for the Coulomb friction is

$$F_{\text{str}, r} = -\mu_C N \text{ sg } v$$

in which $N$ is the force normal to the surface, $\mu_C$ is Coulomb's friction coef-

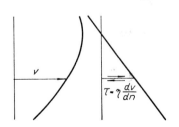

Fig. III-7. Velocity and viscous shear stress distributions in laminar flow

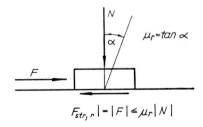

Fig. III-8. Equilibrium of active force $F$ and friction force at rest $F_{\text{str}, r}$

ficient, while $\operatorname{sg} v = +1$, if $v > 0$, $\operatorname{sg} v = -1$, if $v < 0$ and $\operatorname{sg} v = 0$, if $v = 0$. The following is the scale ratio of Coulomb's friction force

$$c_{F_{str,c}} = c_{\mu_c}\, c_N. \tag{VIIb}$$

(c) *Friction linearly proportional to the slip velocity of the structure* (e.g. friction of a bearing):

$$F_{str,\,l} = -\mu_l N v$$

in which $\mu_l$ is the linear friction coefficient (which usually depends on the viscosity within, and the geometry of, the gap).

The scale ratio of the linear friction force:

$$c_{F_{str,l}} = c_{\mu_l}\, c_N\, c_v. \tag{VIIc}$$

It should be noted that in the case of so-called force-free bearings and of certain damping devices, $N$ and $c_N$ do not appear in the friction force equations.

(d) *Friction force proportional with the square of the velocity of the structure movement* (e.g. the resistance of certain damping devices). This type of friction is determined by the relationship

$$F_{str,\,sq} = -\mu_{sq}\, N\, v^2\, \operatorname{sg} v$$

in which $\mu_{sq}$ is the quadratic friction coefficient (as a function of viscosity and of the geometry of the damping device).

The scale ratio of the quadratic friction force, may be written as

$$c_{F_{str,\,sq}} = c_{\mu_{sq}}\, c_N\, c_v^2. \tag{VIId}$$

It should be noted that the kinds of damping used in practice are mostly independent of $N$. In such cases, $N$ and $c_N$ do not occur in the friction relationship.

## 2. Criteria of Dynamic Similitude by Comparison of Force Scale Ratios

For dynamic similarity of the model to the prototype the numerical value of the scale ratios (I–VII) of the afore-listed forces must be identical within a permissible error limit. Therefore, the following set of equations (condition equations) can be written:

$$c_F = c_{F_{inert}} = c_{F_{grav}} = c_{F_{elast}} = c_{F_{turb}} = c_{F_{visc}} = c_{F_{pres}} = c_{F_{str,\,r}} =$$
$$= c_{F_{str,c}} = c_{F_{str,l}} = c_{F_{str,\,sq}} \tag{VIII}$$

from which, for example, the following nine independent equations can be derived:

$$c_{F\text{inert}} = c_{F\text{grav}} \qquad\qquad \text{(IX} \to \text{I=II)}$$

$$c_{F\text{inert}} = c_{F\text{elast}} \qquad\qquad \text{(X} \to \text{I=III)}$$

$$c_{F\text{inert}} = c_{F\text{turb}} \qquad\qquad \text{(XI} \to \text{I=IV)}$$

$$c_{F\text{inert}} = c_{F\text{visc}} \qquad\qquad \text{(XII} \to \text{I=V)}$$

$$c_{F\text{inert}} = c_{F\text{pres}} \qquad\qquad \text{(XIII} \to \text{I=VI)}$$

$$c_{F\text{inert}} = c_{F\text{str, }r} \qquad\qquad \text{(XIV} \to \text{I=VIIa)}$$

$$c_{F\text{inert}} = c_{F\text{str, }c} \qquad\qquad \text{(XV} \to \text{I=VIIb)}$$

$$c_{F\text{inert}} = c_{F\text{str, }l} \qquad\qquad \text{(XVI} \to \text{I=VIIc)}$$

$$c_{F\text{inert}} = c_{F\text{str, sq}} \qquad\qquad \text{(XVII} \to \text{I=VIId)}$$

Substituting the right-hand sides of Eqs (I . . .VII) into Eqs (IX . . .XVII), but with the restriction that $c_g = 1$ and $c_\varrho = 1$ (i.e. $c_\gamma = 1$, in which $c_\gamma$ is the scale ratio of the specific weights of water and solid bodies participating in the phenomena), the following relationships are obtained:

According to Eq. (IX)

$$c_\varrho c^2 c_v^2 = c_\varrho c^3 c_g, \tag{1}$$

which is but an expression of Froude's law [61, 151].

Hence

$$c_v = c^{1/2} c_g^{1/2} = c^{1/2} \tag{2}$$

that is, the scale ratio of velocity equals the square root of the scale ratio of lengths. This criterion can be satisfied, and in open-surface flow and occasionally, depending on the type of structure, in closed section flow, it must be satisfied. Subsequently this will be considered a basic criterion and any deviation from this will be mentioned separately.

The scale ratio of the force itself, either on the basis of Eqs (1) and (2) or directly from Eq. (II), by assuming that $c_\varrho = c_g = 1$, will be

$$c_F = c^3. \tag{2a}$$

According to Eq. (X)

$$c_\varrho c^2 c_v^2] = c_E c^2. \tag{3}$$

After simplifying and combining with Eq. (2)

$$c_E = c_\varrho c_v^2 = c_\varrho (c^{1/2} c_g^{1/2})^2 = c_\varrho c_g c = c; \tag{4}$$

in other words, the elasticity of the materials participating in the phenomenon should be reduced according to the geometrical scale. This needs further consideration since the elasticity of water is beyond control so it is the same in the model as in the prototype, that is, $c_E = 1$, and consequently

54

$c = 1$. This would imply that it is not possible for elastic phenomena to be studied in a reduced model.

For practical reasons, at present, no fluid other than water can be taken into consideration. If liquids are utilized no considerable scale reduction is feasible, with gases the free-surface cannot be realized. In this latter case the very low average density required of the model structures also represents an insuperable obstacle.

According to Eqs (XI) and (IVa)

$$c_\varrho c^2 c_v^2 = c^2 c_v^2 c_\varrho c_g c_C^{-2}, \tag{5}$$

i.e., after reduction:

$$c_C = c_g^{1/2} = 1. \tag{6}$$

This condition can be satisfied by preserving the value of relative roughness if the model, too, is working in the quadratic range of turbulence or in the vicinity of this. On the other hand, Eq. (IVb) of the internal friction is automatically identical with Eq. (I) of the inertia force:

$$c_\varrho c^2 c_v^2 = c^2 c_v^2 c_\varrho \tag{6a}$$

which also demonstrates that turbulent friction is a characteristic inertia force.

According to Eq. (XII)

$$c_\varrho c^2 c_v^2 = cc_v c_v c_\varrho, \tag{7a}$$

that is after reduction and by using Eq. (2)

$$c_v = cc_v = cc^{1/2}c_g^{1/2} = c^{3/2} \tag{7b}$$

implying that the viscosity of the fluid in the model should decrease as the 3/2-th power of the geometrical scale. This needs further consideration since the viscosity of water is difficult to modify even within narrow limits. Thus, as a rule, the scale ratio of the model should be

$$c = c_v^{3/2} \approx 1.$$

According to Eq. (XIII)

$$c_p c^2 = c_\varrho c^2 c_v^2, \tag{8a}$$

whence

$$c_p = c_v^2, \tag{8b}$$

which does not affect any property of the fluid or the structure but implies only that by adopting the scale ratio of velocities on the basis of other considerations, the scale ratio of hydrodynamic pressures also is determined. In open-surface flow where the pressure scale is obviously equal to the water column scale, i.e. to the geometrical scale of linear dimensions, evidently [in agreement with Eq. (2)]:

$$c_p = c_v^2 = c_h = c. \tag{8c}$$

55

On the other hand, in closed-conduit flow the pressure scale and the geometrical scale may be different.

According to Eq. (XIV)

$$c_\varrho c^2 c_v^2 = c_{\mu,r} c_N. \tag{8d}$$

If the force $N$ is created by the flow, its scale ratio is identical with that of the inertia force, i.e. necessarily

$$c_{\mu,r} = 1. \tag{8e}$$

This condition can be fulfilled.

If the force $N$ is independent of the flow and the movement of the structure (e.g. if it is generated by clamp-jaw-like devices), then, also with regard to Eq. (2),

$$c_{\mu,r} c_N = c^2 c_v^2 = c^3 \tag{8f}$$

must be realized. In practice, this is possible if the force $N$ is modelled, like the other forces, to a scale ratio $c^3$, i.e. again the prescription of Eq. (8e) has to be followed.

According to Eq. (XV)

$$c_\varrho c^2 c_v^2 = c_{\mu,C} = c_N. \tag{8g}$$

Applying similar considerations as earlier, the two solutions are either

$$c_{\mu,C} = 1 \tag{8h}$$

or, also taking into account Eq. (2),

$$c_{\mu,C} c_N = c^2 c_v^2 = c^3. \tag{8i}$$

This latter again can be realized as $c_N = c^3$ and $c_{\mu C} = 1$.

According to Eq. (XVI)

$$c_\varrho c^2 c_v^2 = c_{\mu,l} c_N c_v. \tag{8j}$$

Moreover, if the scale ratio of force $N$ is identical with that of the inertia force, also using Eq. (2), then

$$c_{\mu,l} = c_v^{-1} = c^{-1/2} \tag{8k}$$

whose satisfaction, in certain cases, does not seem to be impossible. (The coefficient of bearing friction can be increased by lubricants of higher viscosity, whereas the ability to ensure the adequate gap size is a very difficult problem.) If the force $N$ is applied independently of the flow, then, by using Eq. (2),

$$c_{\mu,l} c_N = c^2 c_v = c^{5/2} \tag{8l}$$

which seems to have a practical solution if

$$c_{\mu,l} = 1 \text{ and } c_N = c^{5/2}. \tag{8m}$$

56

Finally, if the friction is not influenced by the normal force $N$,

$$c_{\mu,l} = c^2 c_v = c^{5/2}. \tag{8n}$$

According to Eq. (XVII),

$$c_\varrho c^2 c_v^2 = c_{\mu,\text{sq}} c_N c_v^2. \tag{8o}$$

If $c_N$ is equal to the scale ratio of the inertia force, then, also utilizing Eq. (2),

$$c_{\mu N} = c_v^{-2} = c^{-1}. \tag{8p}$$

Satisfying this criterion is possible in principle but as a rule it raises difficult problems concerning model techniques. However, the occurrence of this type of friction is hardly likely. The same can be said if $N$ is independent of the flow and of the forces affecting the structure. In this latter case the equation

$$c_{\mu,\text{sq}} c_N = c^2 \tag{8q}$$

needs to be satisfied. In the case when the quadratic friction is independent of the force $N$

$$c_{\mu,\text{sq}} = c^2 \tag{8r}$$

has to be followed, which — between certain scale limits and depending on the construction of the damping device — can be realized.

## 3. Scale Ratios of a Few Important Magnitudes

On the basis of Eqs (1–8) derived earlier, the scale ratios of force $c_F$, of time $c_t$, of discharge $c_Q$, of frequency* $c_N$, of moment $c_M$, and of angles $c_\varrho$ are obtained as follows:

The scale ratio of forces on the basis of Eqs (VIII), (I) and (II) [which corresponds to Eq. (2), too] will be

$$c_F = c_\varrho c^2 c_v^2 = c_\varrho c^2 (c^{1/2} c_g^{1/2})^2 = c_\varrho c_g c^3 = c_\gamma c^3 = c^3 = c_V = c_m, \tag{9}$$

that is, it equals the scale ratios $c_V$ and $c_m$ of volumes and masses, respectively.

The scale ratio of times, as a quantity having the dimension of length per velocity, may be derived from Eq. (2):

$$c_t = c c_v^{-1} = c c^{-1/2} c_g^{-1/2} = c^{1/2} c_g^{-1/2} = c^{1/2}. \tag{10}$$

* Since in the following sections the normal force $N$ for friction will not be dealt with any more, it seems reasonable to apply the same symbol for vibration frequencies.

The discharge is a product of velocity and area, so its scale ratio becomes, from Eq. (2):

$$c_Q = c_v\, c^2 = c^{1/2} c_g^{1/2} c^2 = c^{5/2}. \tag{11}$$

The scale ratio of frequency, as a quantity having the dimension 1/time, is obtained with Eq. (10) as

$$c_N = c_t^{-1} = c^{-1/2} c_g^{-1/2} = c^{-1/2}. \tag{12}$$

Moment is a product of force and length, i.e. by using Eq. (9) its scale ratio becomes

$$c_M = c_F\, c = c^3 c = c^4. \tag{12a}$$

The scale factor of angles as non-dimensional quantities will be the unity:

$$c_\vartheta = 1. \tag{12b}$$

The possibilities of avoiding the limitations imposed on $c$, i.e. the geometrical scale ratio (of linear dimensions), by Eqs (4) and (7b) will be considered later.

## 4. Solution of Difficulties Concerning Elasticity for Girders with Longitudinal and Flexural Vibrations

A rigorous application of Eq. (4) would imply that, since the elasticity of water is evidently beyond control, $c_E = 1$ and thus $c = 1$. It should be clear that a 1 : 1 scale model would mean a prototype investigation which is just what we wish to avoid. But considering that the potential pressure variations do not surpass 1 or 2 atmospheres [since the velocity of vibrations is much lower (by several orders of magnitude), to that of sound], and the variations in the volume of water and air are negligibly small in comparison to the deformation (bending) of the structure,* *Young's modulus for water can be assumed to be either infinitely high or much lower than the actual value.* This consideration is of fundamental importance. Formulated in a different way this means that from the point of view of elasticity, water and air are modelling themselves within very wide scale limits, since the changes in their volume are always negligible in comparison with the deformation (bending, torsion) of the (steel) structures. Consequently, it is sufficient to deal with the correct modelling of *structural elasticity*, to determine therefore

* According to Soviet researchers [126a], in the case of free-surface flow the compressibility of water influences hydrodynamic pressures to an extent less than 10 per cent if $hf/c < 0.225$ in which $h$ is the water depth, $f$ is the frequency and $c$ is the velocity of the propagation of sound. In Hungary, for example, where for the large hydraulic structures $h$ is about 10 m, $f$ lower than 10 Hz and $c$ is around 1000 m/sec, even one half of the quoted limit is not attained.

a certain value $c_E = c > 1$, and to adopt the same $c_E$ as valid for the water and the air. (So far as air is concerned, this statement is valid only for the free atmosphere. For air pockets between water and the structure the elasticity of air may play a considerable role. The similitude method treated in the book can only be applied with due precaution in such cases.)

There are, however, two additional difficulties related to the Young's modulus of the model material. A rather limited choice of natural and synthetic materials is available for such purposes so that the choice of the elasticity scale is limited to a few discrete values. Moreover, the specific weight (and density) of these materials differ from those of the prototype, i.e. $c_\gamma = 1$ for water and air, but $c_{\gamma 1} \neq 1$ for the structure. That is, when keeping perfect geometrical similarity, the scale factor $c_F = c_\gamma c^3$ given in Eq. (9) would be different for water and air, on the one hand, and for the structure on the other, i.e. the principle of dynamic similitude would be violated. (The model would not be similar to the prototype with regard to the vibrating *mass*.)

This difficulty can be overcome in several ways, all requiring substantially that the same average volumetric weight should be realized in both the prototype and the model (Fig. III-9). This can be attained by applying

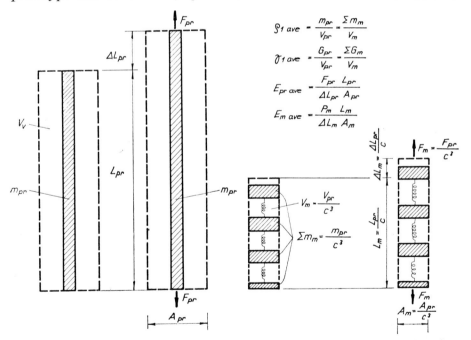

$$\varrho_{1\,ave} = \frac{m_{pr}}{V_{pr}} = \frac{\Sigma m_m}{V_m}$$

$$\gamma_{1\,ave} = \frac{G_{pr}}{V_{pr}} = \frac{\Sigma G_m}{V_m}$$

$$E_{pr\,ave} = \frac{F_{pr}}{\Delta L_{pr}} \frac{L_{pr}}{A_{pr}}$$

$$E_{m\,ave} = \frac{P_m}{\Delta L_m} \frac{L_m}{A_m}$$

$$V_m = \frac{V_{pr}}{c^3}$$

$$\Sigma m_m = \frac{m_{pr}}{c^3}$$

$$F_m = \frac{F_{pr}}{c^3}$$

$$A_m = \frac{A_{pr}}{c^3}$$

Fig. III-9. Sketch of a model element composed of separate masses and springs elastically similar to corresponding prototype element with indication of real and virtual sizes without and under load

59

ballasts or cut-outs. The latter would evidently affect the stress pattern and thus, such methods are in principle approximative ones only. In practice however — and with the necessary care — they can be applied to satisfy completely the requirements of the particular problem. The correct scale ratio of the vibrating mass could also be ensured within a relatively wide range of specific weights. The only question remaining is related to the elasticity of the structure which cannot be solved separately from that of mass. In general, here again a criterion analogous with the foregoing should be satisfied, viz. an average Young's modulus of the homologous space sections should be similar. This can be approximated in several ways:

1. It is possible to design a model combined with springs as in Fig. III-9, which simulates the prototype from the viewpoints of elongation, bending, and torsion [108, 153]. Evidently, the *surface in contact with water must be geometrically similar* to the prototype, wherever its influence on the hydrodynamic effects is not negligible. As a point of departure, this solution has played a decisive role in undertaking the hydroelastic studies on the Nagymaros stop-log (see Chapter VI) but in performing the tests the simpler and more accurate method to be described under point 3 was adopted.

2. Synthetic resin mixed with metal powder was proposed by L. Pálos at the VITUKI laboratory. According to this idea, the proper resin would ensure the required elasticity while the correct quantity of metal powder the necessary specific weight. This method, however, would have required special research in a materials laboratory since its application is not mentioned in the relevant literature.

3. In the course of research at VITUKI in 1964 a solution was developed *which keeps correctly the external form* determining the hydrodynamic load of the structure and which makes it possible to design *a model also correct from the points of view of mass and elasticity,* while ensuring considerable liberty in the choice of the model material. In principle this solution is based on the simple law of elastic strain:

The elongation $dL$ of a bar of length $L$, cross-sectional area $A$ and Young's modulus $E$, extended or compressed by the force $F$ is [143]:

$$dL = \frac{FL}{EA}. \tag{13}$$

This relationship is to be understood for elementary sections $L$ if $F$ and/or $A$ vary in the lengthwise direction. Thus if the contribution of the web plates is ignored, these considerations also apply to flexed girders with flanges.

On the basis of Eq. (13) the relationship between the scale ratios is

$$c = \frac{c_F c}{c_E c_A}. \qquad (13a)$$

Hence

$$\frac{c_F}{c_E c_A} = 1. \qquad (14)$$

The area $A$ can be written as the product of plate width $b$ and plate thickness $s$ (Fig. III-10). To the plate width $b$ the scale ratio $c$ must be applied, since the external surface of the structure in contact with water is determined thereby. The plate thickness $s$, on the other hand, does not influence the hydraulically effective geometry of the cross section and but insignificantly the surface in contact with water. Therefore, between certain limits, an independent scale factor $c_s$ can be determined for plate thickness. Using Eq. (9) and introducing $c_s$, Eq. (14) becomes

$$c_A = c_s c = \frac{c^3}{c_E}, \qquad (15)$$

whence

$$c_s = \frac{c^2}{c_E}. \qquad (16)$$

This means that when calculating the plate thickness by Eq. (16), there are practically no limitations imposed on the elastic properties of the model material nor on the scale and the model can still be designed with the correct elasticity. Nevertheless, the addition of ballast or the reduction in weight (holes), is still necessary to correct the mass and its distribution (Fig. III-11) since, according to Eq. (9), the average weight on unit area of the plates of the structure must be reproduced to the scale factor $c$. The stress distribution and thus the vibrational behaviour of the structure will be least affected by ballast or holes if these are relatively not too large

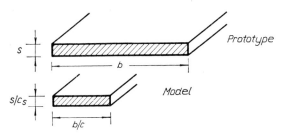

Fig. III-10. A simple plate and its model

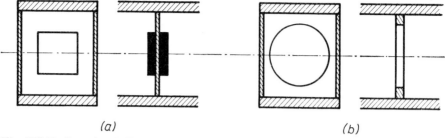

(a)                                        (b)

Fig. III-11. Locating ballasts and cut-outs on rib of a girder

and are concentrated on the ribs which are solely to prevent buckling but not to bear tension, compression, bending or torsion.

The mass of the prototype structure is the sum of the individual plates:

$$m_{pr} = \Sigma \, sb L \, \varrho_1 . \tag{16a}$$

With regard to $c_b = c_L = c$ and $c_{\varrho 1} = c_{\gamma 1}$, as well as by considering Eq. (16), the scale ratio yielding the load-bearing mass $m_t$, will be

$$c_{mt} = c_s c^2 c_{\gamma 1} = c^4 \frac{c_{\gamma 1}}{c_E} . \tag{16b}$$

The ballast $m_b$ necessary in the model is given by the scale factor $c_{mb}$ which is the ratio of the prototype total mass $m_{pr}$ to the model ballast $m_b$. Therefore, the total mass $m_m$ of the model will be:

$$m_m = m_t + m_b = \frac{m_{pr}}{c_{mt}} + \frac{m_{pr}}{c_{mb}} = \frac{m_{pr}}{c^3} . \tag{16c}$$

After rearranging terms

$$\frac{m_{pr}}{c^3} - \frac{m_{pr}}{c_{mt}} = \frac{m_{pr}}{c_{mb}} , \tag{16d}$$

Whence, considering Eq. (16b),

$$c_{mb} = \frac{m_{pr}}{\dfrac{m_{pr}}{c^3} - \dfrac{m_{pr}}{c_{mt}}} = \frac{c^3}{1 - \dfrac{c^3}{c_{mt}}} = \frac{c^4}{c - \dfrac{c_E}{c_{\gamma 1}}} . \tag{16e}$$

Ballast is needed indeed if $c_{mt} > c^3$ (i.e. the load-bearing mass of the model is smaller than the necessary total model mass), otherwise $c_{mb}$ is negative, which means that the mass of the model must be decreased by holes (e.g. on the unloaded ribs). Considering the last term on the right-hand side of Eq. (16e), this statement can be formulated as follows:

62

Ballast is needed if

$$c_{mb} = \frac{c^4}{c - \dfrac{c_E}{c_{\gamma 1}}} > 0 , \tag{16f}$$

that is if

$$c > \frac{c_E}{c_{\gamma 1}} . \tag{16g}$$

Weight reduction is needed (in the form of holes, or relatively lighter ribs) if $c_{mb} < 0$, that is, if

$$c < \frac{c_E}{c_{\gamma 1}} . \tag{16h}$$

Finally, neither ballast nor weight reduction is needed, i.e. the model is correct not only from the point of view of elasticity but also from that of mass if

$$c = \frac{c_E}{c_{\gamma 1}} , \tag{16i}$$

because in this case

$$c_m = \infty . \tag{16j}$$

The plate thickness may also be selected in such a manner that in the case of a given specific weight scale factor $c_{\gamma 1}$, the area-weight (weight/unit area) of the plates (practically the mass of the model structure) should be correct, i.e.

$$G_{pr} = c G_m \tag{17}$$

where $G_{pr}$ is the area-weight of the prototype plates and $G_m$ is that of the model plates, for example in kp/m². Hence, if the thickness of the plates is denoted by $s$, their specific weight by $\gamma_1$, with the prototype and model values being denoted by the subscripts $v$ and $m$, respectively, then

$$s_v \gamma_{1v} = c s_m \gamma_{1m} .$$

Introducing the scale factors

$$c_s s_m \gamma_{1v} = c s_m \gamma_{1m} ,$$

whence

$$c_s \gamma_{1v} = c \gamma_{1m} ;$$

that is

$$c_s = c \frac{\gamma_{1m}}{\gamma_{1v}} = \frac{c}{c_{\gamma 1}} \tag{18}$$

where $c_{\gamma 1}$ is the scale ratio for the specific weight (and density) of the structural material.

If the plate thickness is calculated according to Eq. (18), the *mass* of the model will be correct to scale, but in general it will fail to reproduce *elasticity*.

*The model will be correct with regard to both weight (mass) and elasticity* if the scale factor $c$ is calculated by equating the values $c_s$ obtained from Eqs (16) and (18):

$$\frac{c^2}{c_E} = \frac{c}{c_{\gamma 1}},$$

that is, [obviously in agreement with Eq. (16i)]

$$c = \frac{c_E}{c_{\gamma 1}}. \tag{19}$$

The resulting geometrical scale ratio will not be an integer but the vibrations of the model will be reproduced correctly, according to Eqs (10) and (12), as regards both amplitudes and frequencies.

(As examples it should be noted that for a prototype structure of steel, the correct model scales for different materials would be approximately as follows: 1 : 2.2 for brass, 1 : 12 for hard polyvinylchloride and 1 : 1(!) for aluminium. Viz. the specific weights are: 7.85 p/cm³ for steel, 8.5 for brass, about 1.4 for hard PVC, and 2.7 p/cm³ for aluminium. The Young's moduli are: $2.1 \times 10^6$ kp/cm² for steel, $1.05 \times 10^6$ for brass, about $0.031 \times 10^6$ for hard PVC, and $0.74 \times 10^6$ for aluminium.

In the case of brass as model material, $c_E = 2.1/1.05 = 2$, $c_{\gamma 1} = 7.85/8.5 = 0.92\dot{2}$, that is, $c = 2/0.922 = 2.16 \approx 2.2$.

In the case of a model of hard PVC, $c_E = 2.1/0.031 = 67.9$, $c_{\gamma 1} = 7.85/1.4 = 5.61$, that is, $c = 67.9/5.61 = 12.1 \approx 12$.

For an aluminium model $c_E = 2.1/0.74 = 2.84$, $c_{\gamma 1} = 7.85/2.7 = 2.91$ and so $c = 2.84/2.91 = 0.975 \approx 1$.)

Considering now *flexed girders* specifically, it is important to state that since the internal forces in the flanges also depend on the distance from the neutral axis, from the point of view of elasticity it would be necessary to keep the *axis* of the plates with a distorted-thickness of the model at the position corresponding to geometrical similarity (Fig. III-12). But if the distortion of the plate thickness is considerable, insistence on the correct axis position may change significantly the surface in contact with water and thereby, modify the hydrodynamic conditions too. If, on the other hand, the hydraulically effective (e.g. the outer) surface of the plates is maintained at the position corresponding to geometrical similarity then

Fig. III-12. (a) Geometrically scaled model cross section, (b) Model in which geometry of the axis of cross sections is similar to prototype but plate thickness satisfies elastic similarity, (c) Model cross section which satisfies geometrical similarity of hydraulically important surfaces (outer surfaces in example), while elastic similarity is attained simultaneously by appropriately scaled plate thickness

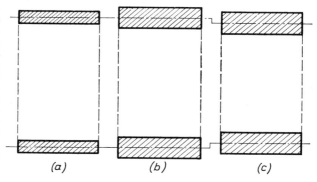

(a)          (b)          (c)

the axis of the plates would be closer to the neutral axis and consequentlu, the internal forces and the deflections of the girder would be greater than those required for structural similarity.

In this case a modified procedure based upon the differential equation of bending may be adopted.

## 5. Improvement of Model Scaling for Flexural Vibrations

The differential equation for the elastic line [143] is:

$$\frac{d^2y}{dx^2} = -\frac{M}{EI} \tag{20}$$

where $x$ is the longitudinal coordinate of an arbitrary point (cross section) of the elastic line, $y$ is the deflection of the line at the afore-mentioned cross section, $M$ is the bending moment at the cross section, and $I$ is the moment of inertia of the cross section about the neutral axis (Fig. III-13).

In terms of scale ratios, considering Eq. (12a) and that the dimension of the left-hand side is 1/length:

$$c^{-1} = c^4 c_E^{-1} c_I^{-1}. \tag{21}$$

Hence

$$c_E c_I = c^5. \tag{22}$$

If the geometrical similarity of the cross section is maintained, that is $c_I = c^4$, Eq. (22) does not introduce any new criterion for $c_E$ in comparison with Eq. (4). But considering that the forces induced by the flow are influenced by the "hydraulically effective geometry" of the structure only rather than by the plate thicknesses, and also that the elastic deformations depend on the moment of inertia of the cross section rather than on the direct geometrical data, a scale ratio differing from that for the other lengths can be used for plate thickness.

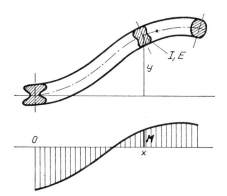

Fig. III-13. Characteristic data of loaded girder

Applying the scale factor $c_s$ of plate thickness $s$

$$c_I = c^3 c_s. \tag{23}$$

It must not be forgotten that once the plate scale ratio is different, the scale ratio of inertia (1), can only be approximate, and (2) is based on the Steiner theorem and thus it is assumed that the distance of the plate axis from the neutral axis obeys the scale factor $c$.

Combining Eq. (23) again with Eq. (22), we arrive at

$$c_E c^3 c_s = c^5, \tag{24}$$

that is, we obtain Eq. (16) which has already been derived in a simpler way*:

$$c_s = \frac{c^2}{c_E}. \tag{25=16}$$

Since the differential equation (20) of the elastic line does not include the plate thickness and the geometrical dimensions of the cross section, the model of correct elasticity can also be designed by arranging the external surfaces in contact with water in a position satisfying geometrical similarity, and then, after assuming the scale ratio $c_E$ of Young's modulus, as well as the scale ratio $c$ which applies to the hydraulically important geometrical dimensions, the cross-sectional area of the plates should be dimensioned according to the scale ratio $c_I$ of inertia [using Eq. (22)]. This latter however, is but an implicit expression of the plate thickness:

$$c_I = \frac{c^5}{c_E}. \tag{26}$$

In this way the external plate surface in contact with water needs to be shaped only according to geometrical similarity, whereas the restrictions

---

* Where an equation has been derived in an alternative manner, this will be reflected in the equation number, e.g. (25 = 16).

Fig. III-14. Moments of inertia of plate cross section about centroidal axis $x$ of girder and about centroidal axis $x'$ of plate itself

$$I_{x'} = k's^3$$

$$I_x \approx ks$$

on the internal structural components are less stringent since these do not affect hydraulic conditions and only the necessary inertia must be attained.

(As an example, it should be mentioned that the elastic properties of the model material for the Nagymaros stop-log have called for considerable plate thicknesses. Thus after orientation by means of Eq. (16), the calculation was performed on the basis of Eq. (26). The proper mass distribution was ensured by mounting ballast on the ribs [71]).

One should be aware of the fact that the model designed according to either Eq. (16) or Eq. (26) will reproduce the movements of the prototype only *as a whole*. The plates in the individual frames will not vibrate to scale, because they will be either too hard (if $c_s < c$), or too soft (if $c_s > c$), viz. when designing the whole girder, the inertia of these plates is taken about the neutral axis $x$ of the girder and depends then on the *first* power of the plate thickness (Fig. III-14). However, when dimensioning the plate sections in the individual frames (by which local vibrations are determined) their inertia is taken about their own axis and this varies as the *third* power of plate thickness. Specifically, since the inertia of the plate about its axis is defined as

$$I = \frac{s^3 b}{12}, \tag{26a}$$

the scale ratio of this inertia will become

$$c_I = c_s^3 c. \tag{26b}$$

Substituting this into Eq. (22)

$$c_E c_s^3 c = c^5, \tag{26c}$$

that is,

$$c_s = \sqrt[3]{\frac{c^4}{c_E}}, \tag{26d}$$

which differs radically from Eq. (26 = 16). That is, the local vibration of the *plate* itself and the vibration of the *whole girder* generally cannot be reproduced in the same model. An exception to this is the case of $c_E = c$, where

$$c_s = \sqrt[3]{\frac{c^4}{c}} = c \qquad (26\text{e})$$

in agreement with the value obtained from Eq. (25):

$$c_s = \frac{c^2}{c_E} = \frac{c^2}{c} = c. \qquad (26\text{f})$$

In this case the right amount of ballast is needed only so that the vibrations of both the whole model and its individual plate sections are reproduced correctly.

(If the numerical data mentioned in connection with Eq. (19) are recalled, it will be realized that it is possible to make a 1 : 2.84 scale model of aluminium which would be elastically similar to the steel prototype so far as both the whole structure and its components are concerned; ballast being necessary only as a means of ensuring the similarity of the mass. For laboratory investigations on smaller structures this scale may result in feasible model sizes.)

Another potential method of modelling the plate vibrations is to build up the individual plates of several layers which are in contact with each other with friction between them minimized. (This has not been realized in practice since no need has arisen for such investigations.) In this way the plates resist local bending but without interaction. Moreover, since their total inertia about their own axis could be arbitrarily smaller than that of a single plate with the same overall thickness and at the same time the inertia about the neutral axis of the whole girder would remain the same, the vibrations of both the whole structure and its individual plate elements could be made similar to those of the prototype.

Replacing the plate of thickness $s$ by $n$ pieces of plate of thickness $s/n$ would reduce the original moment of inertia

$$I = \frac{bs^3}{12} \qquad (26\text{g})$$

(Fig. III-15a) to the value

$$I_n = n\frac{b\left(\frac{s}{n}\right)^3}{12} = \frac{1}{n^2}\frac{bs^3}{12} \qquad (26\text{h})$$

(Fig. III-15b). At the same time, evidently, the scale ratio $c_{In}$ of inertia

68

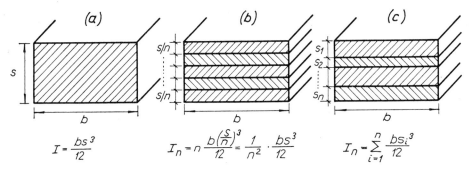

Fig. III-15. Alternative solutions for model plate [(a) compact, (b) sliced into equal thicknesses, (c) sliced into unequal thicknesses] and the respective inertia moments

about its own central axis would be increased by $n^2$ times against the original $c_I$. In agreement with Eq. (26b)

$$c_{In} = c_s^3 \, cn^2 . \qquad (26i)$$

Combining this with Eq. (22):

$$c_E \, c_s^3 \, cn^2 = c^5 , \qquad (26j)$$

whence, introducing also Eq. (25):

$$c_s = \sqrt[3]{\frac{c^4}{n^2 c_E}} = \frac{c^2}{c_E} . \qquad (26k)$$

Raised to the third power:

$$\frac{c^4}{n^2 c_E} = \frac{c^6}{c_E^3} , \qquad (26l)$$

leading to the following simple solution being obtained for $n$:

$$n = \frac{c_E}{c} . \qquad (26m)$$

(Thus a PVC model with a geometrical scale 1 : 23 and with three layers of plates replacing the single prototype plate will reproduce the vibrations of the prototype as regards both the whole structure and the individual plates, provided that internal damping is negligible.)

A flange composed of plates of unequal thickness is also conceivable (Fig. III-15c) and makes more delicate approximations possible. For the plate thicknesses adopted it is expedient to make the calculation an "ad hoc" one.

If the structure consists of *a single plate* and it is also desired to reproduce it by a single plate, similarity cannot be realized unless the rigidity of the plate in one direction can be taken as infinite. Obviously the effect of distorting the plate thickness will be different on the moments of inertia about the two (linear and cubic) axes while the reduction of forces is unrelated to direction. Nevertheless, the foregoing approach, namely "slicing" the plate, may also be found useful in this case. For practical purposes, this is needed only if the two dimensions of the cross section are not too different, as for example, in the case of a beam. But even then a box structure (consisting of four plates) will probably be a much more practical way of achieving the aim.

## 6. Elastic Modelling of Cables and Rods

Besides flexural vibrations, the girder (e.g. movable gate or stop-log) will oscillate as a single mass on the suspension cables (rods), too. The method of modelling the elasticity of the cable is well-known: according to geometrical similarity, the identity of the (relative) strains only need be ensured. The mass of the cable is mostly negligible in comparison with that of the structure, so the specific weight of the cable can be ignored. On the basis of Eqs (14) and (9)

$$c = \frac{c^4}{c_E c_A},\tag{27}$$

thus the scale ratio of the cable cross section will be

$$c_A = \frac{c^3}{c_E}.\tag{28}$$

If the material of the model cable is the same as that of the prototype we have $c_A = c^3$. The strains will be identical if the scale ratios of the force $(c_F = c^3)$ and of the cross sectional area $(c_A)$ are the same.

In cases where neither the cross section nor the Young's modulus of the cable are specified, the strain $\varepsilon = \Delta L/L$ alone is sufficient for designing the model cable. The latter should be dimensioned or selected by trial and error so that under the corresponding load the strain should be the same as in the prototype. This means that if the model cable is subject to a load $F_m = F_{pr}/c^3$, the strain should be equal to that undergone by the prototype cable under the load $F_{pr}$. (The suspension cable of the Nagymaros stop-log model, for example, was dimensioned this way.) Instead of an elastic cable, obviously some other kind of suspension (cantilever, simple beam, etc.) can be applied, provided that its spring constant can be adjusted to the length of the prototype cable (position of the girder).

70

If for any reason the mass of the suspension cable (rod) is not negligible, uniformly distributed ballast (e.g. lead spheres) should be mounted on it. On the other hand, no cable material can be used that would require a reduction of mass, since this could only be realized to the detriment of elasticity. It can be readily demonstrated that the ballast per unit length of cable has the scale ratio:

$$c_{mb} = \frac{W_{pr}}{W_{mb}} = \frac{c^3}{c - \dfrac{c_E}{c_{\gamma 1}}}, \qquad (29)$$

where $W_{pr}$ is the linear weight (e.g. in kp/m) of the prototype cable and $W_{mb}$ is the necessary ballast per unit length in the model. It is apparent that ballast is needed, if Eq. (16g) applies.

The effect of the length must evidently be considered in the case of the afore-mentioned other types of suspensions and, if necessary, this effect must be corrected in such a way that the total inertia of the model should follow the requirements of similitude.

### 7. Designing the Model for Torsional Vibrations

Since, in addition to flexural and longitudinal vibrations, the structure might be subjected to torsional (shearing) vibrations as well, it is necessary to examine the equations of shearing-torsional deformations from the point of view of modelling.

Consider first the case of simple shear (Fig. III-16). If an elementary area $A$ of a cross section of the girder is subject to a shear force $T$, the directions perpendicular to the cross section will be deflected by the angle [21]:

$$\alpha = \frac{1}{G} \cdot \frac{T}{A} \qquad (30)$$

where $G$ is the shear modulus. In a scale-ratio form

$$1 = c_G^{-1} \frac{c^3}{c_A}. \qquad (31)$$

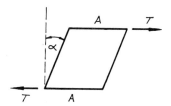

Fig. III-16. Shear and resulting deflection angle

If the cross section of the model is geometrically undistorted, then $c_A = c^2$, and therefore

$$c_G = c, \tag{32}$$

that is, the instruction for reproducing the shear modulus is the same as Eq. (4) for Young's modulus and is in general just as impossible to comply with.

The area $A$ is the product of the length $L$ (in the direction of shear) and the plate thickness $s$ perpendicular to $L$. Equation (31) is rewritten in the form

$$\cdot 1 = c_G^{-1} \frac{c^3}{c_s c}. \tag{33}$$

The scale ratio of the polar moment of inertia $I_p$ is introduced by multiplying by $c^2/c^2$:

$$1 = c_G^{-1} \frac{c^5}{c_s c^3} = c_G^{-1} \frac{c^5}{c_{Ip}}. \tag{34}$$

Hence the scale ratios of plate thickness and of the polar moment of inertia become

$$c_s = \frac{c^2}{c_G}. \tag{35}$$

and

$$c_{Ip} = \frac{c^5}{c_G}, \tag{36}$$

respectively, which are identical in form with Eqs (16) and (18) obtained for elastic strain and bending. Since the polar moment of inertia of any cross section is the sum of the moments of inertia about the two principal axes through the centroid [143], that is,

$$I_p = I_x + I_y, \tag{37}$$

it follows automatically that the scale ratio of the polar moment of inertia is the same as those of the inertia moments about these axes. Consequently, since $c_s$ and $c_{Ip}$ have already been determined in the calculations related to elastic bending, the value of $c_G$ cannot be assumed arbitrarily but, on the basis of Eqs (35) and (36), it must be identical with $c_E$:

$$c_G = c_E. \tag{38}$$

Formulating it in another way, the equality of the ratios

$$\frac{G_v}{E_v} = \frac{G_m}{E_m} \tag{39}$$

must be satisfied for the prototype and the model materials. Materials of practical interest meet Eq. (39) in very fortunate cases only, the ratio $G/E$ varying for these between 0.3 and 0.6. For steel it is 0.395, for Decelith (used for the Nagymaros stop-log model) it is 0.336. Consequently, at present no models reproducing exactly both flexural and torsional vibrations can be built. If, however, the role of the torsional vibrations is insignificant, or the two values of the ratio $G/E$ do not differ too much (which is already possible), the torsional vibrational phenomena can be investigated satisfactorily on the model designed for flexural vibration.

As will be demonstrated in the following, the relationships developed for a rectangular cross-section subject to shear retain their validity for cylindrical bars and for pipes with annular and arbitrary cross section (Fig. III-17), but considerable differences arise in the case of single plates and longitudinally split pipes (Fig. III-18) — similarly to the results obtained for the flexion of single plates.

For bars with circular and annular cross sections [143]:

$$\Phi = \frac{M_t L}{I_p G} \tag{40}$$

where $\Phi$ is the torsional angle of the girder over the (elementary or finite) length $L$; $M_t$ is the torsional moment, which is constant along the length

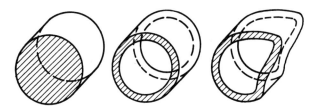

Fig. III-17. Cylindrical bars and pipes

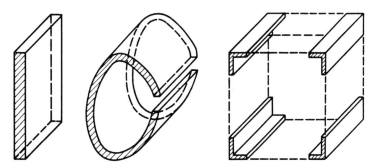

Fig. III-18. Plate and longitudinally split pipes

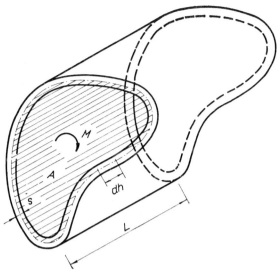

Fig. III-19. Thin-walled pipe with symbols for Bredt equation

$L$; $I_p$ is the polar moment of inertia of the cross section; $G$ is the shear modulus of the structural material. In scale-ratio form:

$$1 = \frac{c^4 c}{c_{Ip} c_G}, \tag{41}$$

hence

$$c_{Ip} = \frac{c^5}{c_G}, \tag{42=36}$$

which is actually identical with Eq. (36). (For solid bars only if $c_G = c$ !)

For thin-walled pipes (not necessarily of circular cross section, see Fig. III-19) — certain sections of the Nagymaros stop-log can be considered such — the Bredt equation [143] yields the angle of torsional rotation:

$$\Phi = \frac{M_g L}{4 G A_k^2} \oint \frac{dh}{s} \tag{43}$$

(where $A_k$ is the area surrounded by the centre line of the pipe wall cross section, $h$ is the length of the centre line of the pipe wall cross section, the other symbols are familiar). The relationship between the scale ratios will be

$$1 = \frac{c^4 c}{c_G c^4} \cdot \frac{c}{c_s} = \frac{c^2}{c_G c_s} = \tag{44}$$

$$= \frac{c^5}{c_G c_s c^3} = \frac{c^5}{c_G c_{Ip}}, \tag{45}$$

whence on the one hand

$$c_s = \frac{c^2}{c_G}, \tag{46=35}$$

on the other hand

$$c_{Ip} = \frac{c^5}{c_G}, \tag{47=36}$$

i.e. the already familiar Eqs (35) and (36) are obtained.

The mass of the model subject to torsional vibrations consists of two parts, like that of the bent girder, and the equations are analogous with those for the latter. For instance, the scale ratio of the load-bearing mass, similarly to Eq. (16b), is

$$c_{mt} = \frac{c^4}{c_G} c_{\gamma 1}. \tag{47a}$$

The necessary ballast (completing mass) can be determined as in the case of the bent girder. The scale ratio of the ballast is

$$c_{mb} = \frac{c^4}{c - \dfrac{c_G}{c_{\gamma 1}}}, \tag{47b}$$

etc.

*For longitudinally split pipes and single thin plates* — certain sections of the Nagymaros stop-log were such — the basic equation for the torsional angle [143] becomes

$$\Phi = 3 \frac{M_t L}{s^3{}_b G}. \tag{48}$$

Hence

$$1 = \frac{c^4 c}{c_s^3 c c_G}. \tag{49}$$

Thus

$$c_s = \sqrt[3]{\frac{c^4}{c_G}}. \tag{50}$$

This equation differs substantially from Eq. (35) and resembles Eq. (25d). (An obvious exception is where $c_s = c$, in which case Eq. (32), that is, $c_G = c$ is obtained, corresponding to the undistorted case.)

This means that split pipes and single plates cannot be modelled for both flexural and torsional efforts simultaneously by distorting the plate thickness. In connection with Eq. (39) it has been mentioned already that the torsional vibrations of the Nagymaros stop-log proved to be insignificant.

75

## 8. Problems Related to Fluid Friction

Equation (7b) can be satisfied, i.e. viscous friction can be reproduced to meet the criterion of dynamic similarity only by modifying the viscosity of the fluid. No suggestion of practical value could be gained in this respect from the relevant literature. In relatively large models it would be possible to control viscosity by heating the water but this method would be energy-consuming, might give rise to accidents and in most cases, make the model itself prohibitively expensive. Problems of water supply would also arise. From a review of the literature and from personal experience it is concluded, however, that the role of viscous friction is rarely significant in the vibrations of either prototype or model hydraulic structures.* Where indicated, the studies on a small-scale model can be completed on a large-scale section model in which better allowance can be made for the viscous effects and the results of which can be used to improve those obtained on the model of the whole structure.

*Where the effect of gravity is not predominant* (as, for example, in several cases of closed-conduit flow), the similitude of viscosity is relatively easier to realize or to approximate. This case will be treated in Section 10.

## 9. Role and Modelling Possibilities of Structural Friction in Hydroelasticity

The various kinds of structural frictions are important because of their vibration damping effect. Modelling the friction coefficients is not impossible but, depending on their type (as dealt with in Section III. 1), it tends to be difficult, requires intuition, "ad hoc" ideas and a high standard in workshop technique.

Nevertheless, experience and fundamental considerations show that in very many cases the structural damping only slightly influences the prototype vibrations continuously induced by the flow. The designer of the model is right therefore, if he strives to eliminate all kinds of friction instead of modelling them (since because of seemingly insignificant errors in shop-work, frictions several times higher than required may be produced). Such elimination is on the safe side from the viewpoint of discovering potential sources of resonance as the most important problem. As a damping effect

* This book was already in the press when, in 1977, at the XVIIth IAHR Congress, Abelev presented a paper on hydrodynamic damping [5a]. His experimental results also proved that the contribution of viscous and wave damping to the total damping of the vibrations of a hydraulic structure can be ignored. At the same time the "vortex" (square) damping and the structural damping should and can be modelled according to Frounde's law or Euler's law.

the internal damping of the structure and that of the water are still maintained.

So far as the modelling of internal damping is concerned, contradictory information is to be met in the literature. The damping in the model is, according to some references, smaller, according to others, higher than hydraulic similarity would require [46, 76, 99]. Theoretically speaking, the problem has not been satisfactorily elucidated. If we take into account the available model materials, the structural damping would have to be relatively higher, the damping of water again relatively lower than required by the scale. The first statement seems to be definitely confirmed, the latter one less so. Since the question is not settled, further thorough studies are necessary.

## 10. Modelling Hydroelastic Vibrations if Gravitational Force is Not Dominant

Inertia and elastic forces dominate all vibrational phenomena. Roles played by the other forces listed in Section III. 1 are in general less important. In certain cases, however, *the effect of gravity on the phenomena is negligible* (or precisely nil), even where the flow is maintained by gravity, but in the section studied gravity acts only indirectly, through pressure.* For this very reason it is possible both in principle and in practice to reproduce pressure to a scale different from that of the geometrical dimensions.

### 10.1 Models Made of Prototype Material

Where the flow cross section is a perfectly closed one and the centre of gravity of the structure performs rectilinear movement only (or is motionless), gravity will no longer remain predominant. This opens up several modelling possibilities.

Starting from the identity of the scale ratios for inertia and elastic forces, when

$$c_\varrho c^2 c_v^2 = c_E c^2 , \qquad (3{=}50\text{a})$$

we arrive at

$$c_v = \sqrt{\frac{c_E}{c}}. \qquad (50\text{b})$$

---

* For example, the movement of a tubular turbine mounted in a horizontal pipe and carefully balanced is not influenced by the force of gravity. If, however, one blade of the turbine breaks and the centre of gravity gets displaced from the axis of rotation, the force of gravity already influences the movement. Its extent in a specified case may be insignificant but it has to be checked separately. In the case of a turbine rotating around a vertical axis the gravity force will not influence the movement even if one of the blades breaks.

Apart from the same fluid, the use of the same structural material may also be found to be desirable, that is, $c_E = c = c_{y1} = 1$ (which ensures the similarity of mass as well), but then the corresponding velocities in the prototype and in the model must be equal:

$$c_v = 1 .$$ (50c)

The reproduction of the turbulent friction, as to be seen from Eqs (5) and (6), is unaffected by this assumption (provided that the model is also in the turbulent range).

Modelling viscous friction requires that Eq. (7a) holds:

$$c_\varrho c^2 c_v^2 = cc_v c_\nu c_\varrho .$$ (50d=7a)

However, since $c_v = 1$

$$c = c_\nu .$$ (50e)

Since water is also used in the model, that is, $c_\nu = 1$, a 1 : 1 model would be required:

$$c = 1 .$$ (50f)

This implies that no allowance for viscous forces can be made in scale models and the reproduction thereof must be ignored, or conversely, a model can only be used if the viscous forces are negligible.

Under prototype conditions, however, the viscous forces are negligible in the great majority of cases and this refers mostly to the model as well. Although the Reynolds number is lower than in the prototype, this is due exclusively to the reduction of the hydraulic radius since the velocities are identical.

The scale ratio of hydrodynamic pressures, on the basis of Eqs (8b) and (50c), will be

$$c_p = c_v^2 = 1 ,$$ (50g)

that is, the prototype pressure (or at least the prototype hydrodynamic pressure) must be produced in the model. (This means that the pressure and hydrodynamic pressure do not follow the geometrical scale !)

It follows from the above that in closed-conduit flow, if $c_v = 1$, $c_p = 1$ and, furthermore, if the model is made of prototype material and observing geometrical similarity (plate thicknesses included), then its elastic behaviour will also be similar, i.e. not only the vibrations of the whole structure, but also those of the individual structural parts in it can be studied.

78

## 10.2 Models Made of Arbitrary Material

The realization of prototype velocities according to Eq. (50c) is obviously very difficult in a hydraulic laboratory. However, the use of a different material for the model offers very wide possibilities. In fact, if $c_E \neq 1$ (but geometrical similarity is retained and mass similarity is ensured by applying additional masses), then on the basis of Eq. (50b)

$$c_v = \sqrt{c_E} \tag{50h}$$

will ensure hydroelastic similarity. It is obvious that the viscous forces are still not reproduced since from Eqs (50h) and (7) a need for increasing size would follow, which cannot be a practical solution:

$$c = \frac{c_v}{\sqrt{c_E}} = \frac{1}{\sqrt{c_E}} < 1. \tag{50i}$$

Assuming, however, that the viscous forces remain negligible [turbulent friction being still reproduced correctly on the basis of Eqs (5) and (6)], the scale ratio of hydrodynamic pressure will be, from Eqs (8b) and (50h):

$$c_p = c_v^2 = c_E, \tag{50j}$$

which is much easier to realize than the alternative suggestion of Eq. (50g).

If, for example, the model is to be made of aluminium and to the geometrical scale ratio $c = 20$, then, assuming steel to be the prototype material $c_E = 2.84$, and the pressures will be reduced by this scale while the velocities by $\sqrt{c_E} = 1.68$. (A prototype head of 2.84 m would be 1 m in the model.) Similarity of the model mass must be ensured by the addition of ballast. On the basis of the foregoing, this should present no difficulties in calculation.

Should it prove impossible to adopt a velocity scale compatible with the Young's modulus of the model material available, the afore-mentioned *method of modifying the plate thickness can be applied logically* and within the limits quoted there. It should be noted, however, that in the absence of this last modification the method is exact as regards structural elasticity and does not involve any simplifications. Thus, for example, torsion and vibration of the individual parts are as correctly reproduced as if the model were built of the prototype material.

The conclusions arrived at in Subsections 10.1 and 10.2 imply that in cases where no gravity effects are present the vibrations can be reproduced correctly for both the whole structure and its component parts, regardless of the material adopted for the model (which is geometrically similar to the prototype and may be ballasted as well). It is essential, however, that the viscous forces should be negligible, i.e. the flow must be turbulent in the model, too.

*With structures considered rigid on elastic suspension,* Eq. (50h) allows practically free choice of the velocity scale, since suspension elasticity is wholly unaffected (within the elastic limit) by the geometrical and material restrictions, its effect on flow being zero in practically all cases. Thus, among others, a velocity scale ratio $c_v = c^{1/2}$ is also possible which corresponds to the Froude law and enables the simultaneous reproduction of flow at the junction of closed conduits and open channels. It is the only method for modelling structures in closed-conduit flow, if their centre of gravity moves along a curved path whose vertical projection is other than zero, since in this case the influence of gravity cannot be excluded. The model can be dimensioned by using the approach described in the former subsections. The scale factor $c_v = c^{-1}$ satisfying the Reynolds law may also be applied, but only if gravity is negligible.

To complete the remarks in Section III. 6 on the dimensioning of suspension cables the reproduction of the spring constant in general will be described below.

The law expressing the force of the suspension is

$$\Delta L = DF,\tag{50k}$$

where $F$ is the force causing the displacement $\Delta L$, and $D$ is the spring constant. Written into scale-ratio form

$$c = c_D c_F.\tag{50l}$$

Since $c_F = c_p c^2$, its combination with Eqs (8b) and (50l) yields

$$c_D = c_p^{-1} c^{-1} = c_v^{-2} c^{-1}.\tag{50m}$$

Thus, for any given velocity scale the spring constant of the model can be calculated. Where the spring constant of the model is given, the velocity scale is obtained by rearrangement as:

$$c_v = \frac{1}{\sqrt{cc_D}}.\tag{50n}$$

### 10.3 Simultaneous Consideration of Viscous and Turbulent Frictions

If selecting as the starting equation the identity of the scale ratios for viscous and turbulent friction Eq. (7a):

$$c_\varrho c^2 c_v^2 = cc_\nu c_v c_\varrho,\tag{50o = 7a}$$

then the scale ratio form of the well-known Reynolds model law is obtained as:

$$c_v = \frac{c_\nu}{c}.\tag{50p}$$

According to this equation the velocity in the reduced model must be increased over that in the prototype since the fluid is water in both systems ($c_\nu = 1$):

$$c_v = c^{-1}. \tag{50q}$$

Returning to Eq. (3) for the introduction of elasticity, i.e.

$$c_\varrho c^2 c_v^2 = c_E c^2 \tag{50r=3}$$

and combining it with Eq. (50m) we have

$$c_E c^2 = 1. \tag{50s}$$

The geometrical scale ratio thus becomes

$$c = \sqrt{\frac{1}{c_E}}. \tag{50t}$$

A model of the prototype material must be built to the scale 1 : 1, or if any other material is envisaged and the prototype is made of steel, the model must be enlarged. Such problems are conceivable outside the field of hydrotechniques, where for some reason vibration in laminar flow may occur and the Young's modulus of the prototype material is low.

With structures considered rigid, the situation is very much different because only the rigidity of the suspension must be increased over that in the prototype.

It should be noted that in this method of modelling the turbulent friction is also reproduced correctly since the validity of Eq. (6) is not impaired thereby. This also follows from the fact that turbulent friction belongs to the inertia forces and the similarity thereof has been ensured at the outset.

Equation (8b), with consideration to Eq. (50q), will take the form

$$c_p = c^{-2}, \tag{50u}$$

that is, the pressure in the model increases as the square of the geometrical scale ratio. An interesting feature worthy of note is that the corresponding forces in the model and in the prototype are identical, i.e. the scale ratio of the forces is

$$c_F = c_p c^2 = 1. \tag{50v}$$

As seen from the foregoing, elastic modelling with allowance for viscous friction is difficult to realize and there is no need for it. Nevertheless, the principal relationships are believed to be of interest, since in the model designed by these the vibrations induced in the structure and its parts by the effects of forces due to gravity, inertia, elasticity and viscous and turbulent friction, all develop similarly to the prototype vibrations.

# IV. Experimental Verification of the Method of Hydroelastic Similitude

## 1. Introduction

Before 1964, when the method of hydroelastic similitude — the main topic of this book — was developed by the author, only very few utilizable publications had appeared on the fundamentals and techniques of hydroelastic modelling of hydraulic structures. Some of the investigations reported were carried out on a scale of 1 : 1 and some of them on *rigid* model structures with elastic suspension. In addition, mostly closed-conduit flow was treated (cases of certain bottom outlet works) when the role of gravity can usually be ignored. The researchers of the Delft Hydraulic Laboratory were the only ones who performed investigations on *elastic models* and *with regard to gravity*. In 1959, Kolkman published a fundamental paper, concerning these studies and the modelling principles applied [99]. This, in fact, went unnoticed in professional circles for a long while.

Heller's great comprehensive study of 1964 [87] makes no mention of modelling although at the congresses in Montreal and London of the International Association for Hydraulic Research (1959 and 1963, respectively), a number of papers were presented on hydroelastic modelling and even in the field of naval architecture, as pointed out in Subsection II. 1.2, a considerable activity in hydroelastic modelling began [108, 117].

Even in 1969 many researchers still considered it practically impossible to satisfy the Froude law on an elastic model. Several research workers measured pressure oscillations on fixed or artificially oscillated models and from these measurements they drew conclusions on the natural vibration phenomena to be expected. Naturally, there were reasons for the existence of those methods, in discovering the basic mechanisms of the phenomena; moreover, considerable results have been obtained [148a]; however, if the problem concerns an individual structure, then at present only scale models taking all predominating forces into consideration are able to supply a satisfactory answer.

In Hungary it was in connexion with the large river barrages that the need for carrying out hydroelastic model experiments arose on the part of the designers. Such experiments were performed in the VITUKI Hydraulic Laboratory, at first between 1958 and 1962, on rigid models with elastic suspension [54, 55, 56]. Later on, after the most important details of a satisfactory hydroelastic similitude method (see Chapter III) had been independently developed by the author in 1964, in 1964–65 hydroelastic investigations on the model of a stop-long designed for the Nagymaros Barrage were successfully performed [65, 71].

The afore-mentioned method, together with several additions also treated in Chapter III, is based on fundamental laws of absolute validity and allows only well-justified neglections and therefore needs no experimental verification. It is for this reason that it was immediately applied to practical problems. The *measure* of the effect of the neglections made, however, is very important in practice and thus any investigation aiming at the comparison between actually measured prototype data and those transferred from model experiments on the basis of theoretical deductions is extremely important.

Papers on the results of model experiments have already been found in large numbers in the literature. The International Association for Hydraulic Research itself has dealt with hydroelastic problems at four* of its congresses (1959: Montreal, 1963: London, 1965: Leningrad, 1971: Paris) and in two of its Seminars (1970: Stockholm, 1972: Karlsruhe). The subject was touched upon at other meetings, too, and it is a topic which will demand attention for a considerable time. In spite of all this there have been only a few papers analysing in detail the results obtained in different scales and there are not many more alluding at least to a "good agreement between model and prototype". Because of this it seemed to be worth-while carrying out systematic experimentation, in 1968/69 in the Iowa Institute of Hydraulic Research and in 1970/71 in the VITUKI Hydraulic Laboratory, on the hydroelastic behaviour of an elastic cantilever beam modelled to five different scales.

In the following, these experiments and a few other important comparative investigations found in the literature will be treated.

## 2. Study of a Cantilever Model Series

### 2.1 The Models

It seemed evident that the closeness of relationships between model and prototype is a function of the scale,** therefore it was decided to carry out an experiment involving several scale models of the same structure and

---

* While this book was in the press, a fifth congress of IAHR (Karlsruhe, 1977), dealt with hydroelastic problems.

** Referring to the scale naturally means that certain neglected forces are in reality not that negligible and the greater the deviation from the 1 : 1 scale, the greater the contribution of these neglected forces to the predominant forces. Since this addition is not incorporated in the model law (established with regard to the predominant forces only), flow phenomena (including frequencies and amplitudes) influenced by
$\longrightarrow$

possibly covering the entire scale range likely to be used for the hydroelastic modelling of hydraulic structures.

A basic viewpoint of the choice of the structure to be investigated was that its configuration partly be closely related, in respect of the character of the flow phenomena caused by it, to the structures used in engineering practice, and at the same time it should be simple in performance with neither the design nor the construction being unnecessarily complicated because of structural details.

The related literature shows that in the course of research on bodies submerged in the flow, mainly the flow around rigidly fixed bodies was investigated which does not belong in the field of hydroelasticity, i.e. in the sphere of the interaction phenomena between elastic bodies and water.

Certainly, these investigations have concerned many angular bodies, yielding results of value from the viewpoint of hydraulic engineering practice. The spectrum of *elastically suspended, though rigid bodies* is also rather wide, since in this respect the investigation of several individual structures has been carried out; investigations with scientific pretensions, however, have been performed almost exclusively on prismatic bodies in closed-conduit flow, mainly on *circular cylinders*. Finally, as for the *elastic bodies* put in the flow, so far the investigations concerning the Hagestein weir and its 1 : 20 scale elastic model by the Delft Hydraulic Laboratory have been the only ones to give detailed information on the applicability of elastic models dimensioned with gravity effects also taken into account [66, 99, 100, 163], these investigations involving a quite detailed treatment of the theoretical foundations of hydroelastic modelling.

There was no doubt about the necessity for investigations on a structure of angular cross section located in open-surface flow. Finally, a decision was made in favour of a *vertical cantilever of rectangular cross section clamped at its upper end, with the lower end submerging into an open-surface flume and exposed there to hydrodynamic effects*. The joint sketch of the models with non-dimensional (relative) sizes is shown in Fig. IV-1. The investigation of one wood and three lucite models was performed in Iowa, that of a steel model in Budapest.

The illustrations (Fig. IV-2, 3, 4) show the largest lucite model, the wooden model and the steel model built in the respective experimental flume.

-------

these forces neglected in the model become more and more distorted. In the case of the cantilever test series to be presented, the consequences of neglecting viscous friction, structural damping, and — in the case of the smallest model — also capillarity are the most conspicuous.

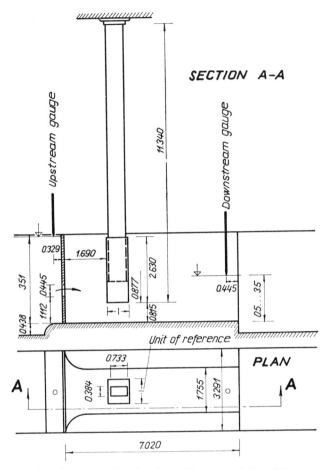

Fig. IV-1. Common sketch of cantilever models with non-dimensional (relative) sizes. (Cantilever is in assembling position "a".)

At first, the wooden model was considered as the largest one, therefore it was and here it will be treated as a 1 : 1 scale model. Based on this, the scales of the lucite models were 1 : 4.06, 1 : 10.2 and 1 : 16.3. Construction of the steel model was decided later, its scale — compared again to the wooden model — was 1.58 : 1.

In the course of the following presentation of our results, the notation of the models by their respective scales will be used according to the above. It should be noted, however, that if the steel model is considered as a prototype (1 : 1), the scales of the others will be 1 : 1.58, 1 : 6.4, 1 : 16.1 and 1 : 25.8. This range of scales satisfies almost perfectly all practical needs, at least for steel structures, since hydraulically loaded steel structures rarely

Fig. IV-2. 1 : 4.06 cantilever scale model of lucite in one of glass flumes of Iowa Institute of Hydraulic Research (IIHR)

Fig. IV-3. 1 : 1 wooden model in IIHR viewed from downstream at medium downstream level

Fig. IV-4. 1.58 : 1 steel model in VITUKI laboratory viewed steeply downward from upstream side. Robust concrete construction ensured a practically absolutely rigid clamping of cantilever. Boards in the middle served communication and mounting purposes

have spans wider than 25 to 30 metres. Moreover, in larger laboratories such as, for example, the VITUKI laboratory, the construction of models with spans of 1 or 1.5 metres together with the necessary flume and the crucial need for discharge do not create any difficulty.

Dimensioning of the models was carried out on the basis of the principles and criteria treated in Chapter III with due consideration to elasticity and mass distribution. No calculation will be detailed here. A similar calculation was published in connection with the Nagymaros stop-log [77]. The trunk of the cantilever was dimensioned from the point of view of elasticity on the basis of Eq. (26), while its mass and mass per unit length followed the scale ratios $c^3$ and $c^2$, respectively. Geometrical similitude was also observed concerning the cross section of the cantilever trunk though here it was not needed, since the trunk was never to submerge. The only thing requiring some explanation is in connection with the seemingly strange scale values.

From the models, the trunks were constructed first to scales 1 : 1, 1 : 4, 1 : 10, 1 : 16 and 1.6 : 1, in accordance with the designs. In the course of a precise checking of the elasticity of the trunks, it was found that the elasticities corresponded to scales 1 : 1, 1 : 4.06, 1 : 10.2, 1 : 16.3 and 1.58 : 1. The trunks were then cut to length according to these modified scales; the new scales were also followed with regard to the sizes of the "box" mounted at the lower end of the cantilevers. The ballast was also dimensioned according to these scales. Subsequently, the cross section and all significant dimensions of the flumes, the discharges, water levels, etc. were adjusted to these scales, too. As an additional explanation to Fig. IV-1. it should be noted that the reference length of all nondimensional lengths was the horizontal edge length of the "box" which constituted the submerged lower part of the cantilever. For the steel model its value was $d = 36.46$ cm. The length of this model was 412.5 cm, the weight 112 kiloponds.

## 2.2 The Measurements and their Evaluation

The principal measurements concerned the natural vibrations of the cantilever models in air and in still water and the vibrations induced by flowing water.

As for the measurement techniques and preliminary tests, the relevant details have been published [73, 75, 83]. Here, the techniques for vibration measurements and the problem deriving from the internal damping of the model material will be described.

The movements of the lower end of the cantilever beam were measured by *strain gauges* glued to the middle of the side plates of the trunk near the upper end. This method can be applied if the beam does not perform upper harmonics or other secondary vibrations, since it is only in this case that the curvature, i.e. the strains at the root are linearly proportional to the displacements of the lower end.

It is known [9] that higher modes decay faster than the basic vibration, since they are nonharmonic. Also, the particular arrangement promoted hardly if any development of higher modes. The strain measurement therefore, gave reliable data on the displacements.

(Model measurements have proved that even the secondary vibrations created by striking the middle of the trunk quite strongly decay very quickly (Fig. IV-5) and in practical cases where hydrodynamic forces act only upon the lower end of the cantilever, such secondary vibrations need not be taken into consideration at all.)

88

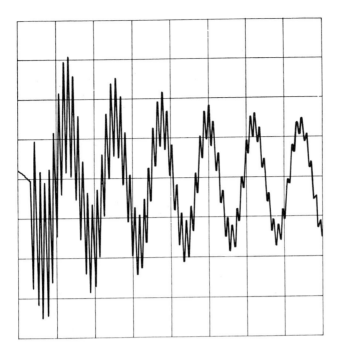

Fig. IV-5. Decay of vibration produced by a single strong pulse load upon middle of cantilever. Comparatively faster decay of secondary vibrations is clearly demonstrated

The elastic similarity of the models has been ensured on the basis of deflection measurements. This simply means, according to model law that, if the force applied is inversely proportionate to the cube of the scale, the deflections of the model must be linearly proportional to this.

When using the lucite models, the *magnitude* of deflection was not single-valued. Under load the cantilever first suffered a practically *instantaneous* deflection which increased with time and in certain cases eventually exceeded — by more than 10 per cent — the initial instantaneous value. Since the expected value of the frequency was around 5 cycles per second even in the 1 : 1 model, and evidently higher in the smaller ones, slow deflection was neglected in the elasticity calculations, and the models were designed with elasticity values calculated from the instantaneous deflections. These models will be called "of statically similar elasticity".

Thus the models of statically similar elasticity suffered (within short periods) deflections corresponding, in principle, to geometrical similarity but measurements have shown the natural frequencies in air to deviate slightly (up to 10–20 per cent) from those calculated from the 1 : 1 model values. (The lucite models came to rest after fewer oscillations than the wooden model.) It is evidently not connected with the higher value of the internal damping of the materials applied but is a consequence of the fact that it was very difficult to determine the deflection just after having put the load on the beam, and the natural frequency shows that instead of the "right" deflection rather a somewhat larger value was measured, i.e. the material acted, in fact, as if it were softer than it behaved at free vibration.

The movement of the submerged model is, however, attenuated not only by the internal, but also by hydraulic damping. According to the literature the latter is much higher than the former. It was therefore decided to start investigations with statically similar elasticity models. Later, however, the trunks of the lucite models were weakened slightly so that their natural frequency in air corresponded to the similarity criteria. Subsequently, measurements were also made on these models "of dynamically similar elasticity".

During the measurements, the *natural vibration* in air was investigated first. The result is the *natural frequency f in air* and the *damping in air*. Damping in air can be characterized by the logarithmic decrement or by the *linear damping factor*, i.e. the ratio $r$ of two subsequent amplitudes, when, as in the present case, the envelope of the oscillogram may be taken with good approximation for an exponential curve (Fig. IV-6). In order to decrease the effect of measurement errors in this case, one may take the

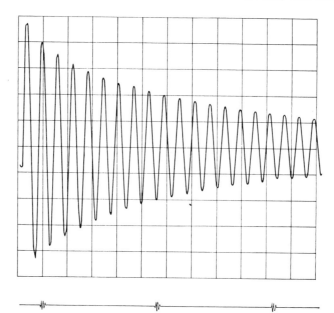

Fig. IV-6. One of oscillograms of natural vibration of 1 : 1 model in air

ratio of two more distant amplitudes under the corresponding root, i.e. if the $i$th double amplitude after the $0$th is denoted by $q_i$, then

$$r = \frac{q_0}{q_1} = \frac{q_{i-1}}{q_i} = \sqrt[n]{\frac{q_0}{q_n}}.$$

In these investigations, data were processed for groups of 10 vibrations and the linear damping factor was thus

$$f = \sqrt[10]{\frac{q_0}{q_{10}}}.$$

The measurements in air were followed by similar ones *in still water* with different water levels. Damping of the vibrations does not follow a simple law here. A characteristic frequency can be readily identified but damping, particularly at greater depths, can only be determined by fitting to the peaks of the oscillogram a pair of envelope curves (Fig. IV-7) and by reading at the $0$th and $10$th vibrational displacements the segment between the two envelopes. The scatter will thus be greater, otherwise the procedure is the same as before.

In the third part of the investigations the vibrations excited by *flowing water* were measured. Here the *flow-induced average frequency* $n$ and the *flow-induced average double amplitude* $\varDelta$, measured at the lower end of the cantilever, are the most characteristic magnitudes, to be calculated at the

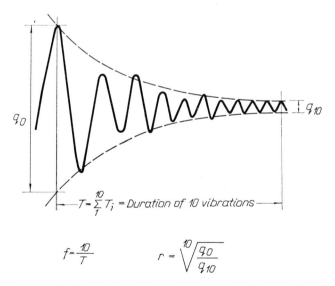

Fig. IV-7. Determination of characteristics of damped natural vibration from oscillogram

91

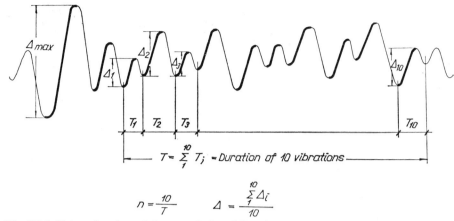

$$n = \frac{10}{T} \qquad \Delta = \frac{\sum\limits_{1}^{10} \Delta_i}{10}$$

Fig. IV-8. Determination of characteristics of flow-induced vibrations from oscillogram

same time most easily. These magnitudes were usually also determined for groups of 10 vibrations (Fig. IV-8). As regards $\Delta$, however, the absolute maximum for each flow condition (constant headwater, different tailwater levels) was found from the oscillograms. At certain conditions the frequency and amplitude spectra were also compared.

All these measurements were carried out for *two different* (assembling) *positions* of the cantilever and for *two vibrational directions* in each position.

The two assembling positions of the cantilever were justified by the different moments of inertia of the trunk cross section in the two principal directions. (In this way the number of the alternatives tested was increased.)

The assembling position has been denoted by "a" if the wider side of the trunk is parallel to the flow. In the other assembling position denoted by "b" it is perpendicular thereto.

The axis of the trunk cross section parallel to the wider sides (i.e. about which the inertia of the cross section is smaller) has been denoted by "0". The other axis is perpendicular thereto and is called axis "1". At each assembling position vibrations perpendicular to the "0" axis and to the "1" axis have been distinguished.

For measurements in air, only the direction of vibration, for those in water both the direction of vibration and the assembling position are essential. The processing of data was carried out in a dimensionless form in order to ensure general validity. Besides the linear damping already known, the dimensionless variables were based on a characteristic dimension, the box edge length $d$, of the geometrically similar models.

During each experimental run the upstream (headwater) level was kept constant at height $h_u$ above the bottom of the contracted flume (Fig. IV-1).

92

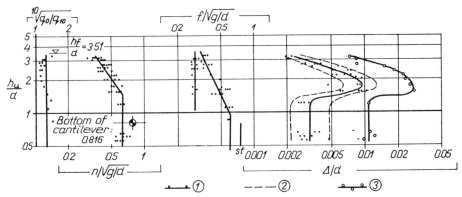

Fig. IV-9. Results of cantilever measurements. Scale = 1 : 16.3. Mounting position: "a". Vibration perpendicular to axis "0". *Legend:* 1 — average of amplitude averages of tenfold vibrations; 2 — maximum and minimum of amplitude averages of tenfold vibrations; 3 — maximum amplitude within the measurement series

In accordance with geometrical similarity, the relative upstream depth had the same value for all models (Fig. IV-1):

$$\frac{h_u}{d} = 3.51$$

Since both the geometry and the headwater level were constant, the flow conditions, velocities, discharge, and vibrations may be defined by a single flow parameter. This is simply the downstream depth $h_d$ measured at the section shown in Fig. IV-1.* The relative downstream depth, $h_d/d$, is the dimensionless parameter in terms of which all other variables were expressed in figures similar to Fig. IV-9. (In these figures the value $h_d/d$ has been entered on the ordinate, while the other magnitudes have been plotted as abscissae.)

The first magnitude in the series of diagrams of Fig. IV-9 is the *linear damping factor* and is already familiar.

$$r = \sqrt[10]{\frac{q_0}{q_{10}}}.$$

The dimension of the natural frequency $f$ is 1/time, its unit is 1/sec (= cycles per second). The situation is the same with the flow-induced

---

* This means that the level of flowing water along the box was different, mostly lower (with the exception of the headwater side of the box) than at the measurement section.

frequency $n$. The dimensionless quantities applied are the relative natural frequency (in the third diagram of Fig. IV-9):

$$\frac{f}{\sqrt{g/d}}$$

and the flow-induced relative frequency (in the second diagram of Fig. IV-9):

$$\frac{n}{\sqrt{g/d}}.$$

Finally the dimensionless ratio, characteristic for the double amplitude $\Delta$, the relative double amplitude

$$\Delta/d$$

has been plotted in the fourth diagram of Fig. IV-9.

The full circles of Fig. IV-9 denote average values calculated for groups of 10 vibrations, while in the amplitude diagrams, empty circles denote the widest amplitudes in a measurement run comprising 200 to 300 vibrations.

It should be noted that the curves bearing no special notation refer to models with dynamically similar elasticity. The curves relating to models

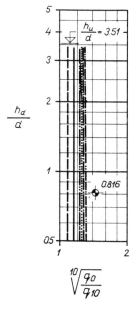

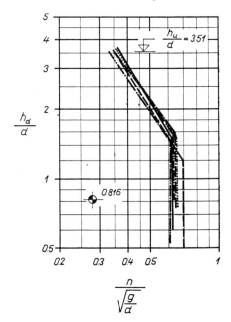

Fig. IV-10. Linear damping factors of five models in air and in stationary water vs. relative tailwater depth. For symbols, see Fig. IV-13

Fig. IV-11. Relative natural frequencies of the five models in air and still water vs. relative tailwater depth. For symbols, see Fig. IV-13

with statically similar elasticity are distinguished by the notation "st". It is important to emphasize, however, that 1 : 1 and 1.58 : 1 models belong to both categories simultaneously.

From among the measurement results, only the comparative diagrams (Figs IV-10–13) for vibrations measured in the direction perpendicular to axis "0" in mounting position "a" will be presented in detail.

Figure IV-10 shows the scattering of the linear damping $r$. The linear damping of the individual models, irrespective of scattering, can be approximated as constant (Fig. IV-9, left side diagram). Actually, there is no difference between the values measured in air and water.

A similarly slight deviation was experienced between the respective linear damping factors of models with statically and dynamically similar elasticity. The only tendency definitively recognizable was the dependence on the material: viz. the damping factor of lucite models is characteristically higher than those of wooden and steel models.

As for the last of these, it is somewhat surprising to find that the damping of the steel model is higher than that of the wooden models. This is due to the fact that in the course of vibration the 1 mm thick steel plate underwent slight buckling, especially near the root where the stresses were high. As a

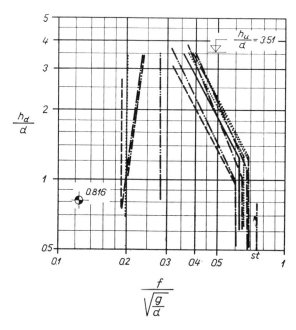

Fig. IV-12. Flow-induced relative frequencies of the five models vs. relative tailwater depth. For symbols, see Fig. IV-13

**95**

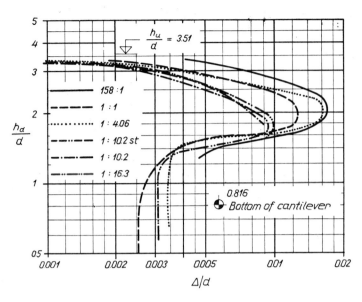

Fig. IV-13. Relative double amplitudes of the five models vs. relative tailwater depth

corrective measure, stiffening ribs (Fig. IV-4) were used, also for ensuring thus a linear relationship between the displacement of the cantilever end and the strain measured by the gauges, but obviously closely spaced ribs along the entire length would have modified perceptibly the flexural elasticity and the vibration frequency alike. Considerable energy was thus consumed by the work of buckling. Finally, the average values of the linear damping factor remained within a margin of 20 per cent.

Considering a conventional steel structure with plates thick enough to exclude any buckling under normal conditions, the linear damping factor may be as low as 1.01 according to data published in the literature. In contrast to this, the damping factor of any model material is higher. The present measurements have provided more definite values on these, i.e., the linear damping factor of a lucite or plexi model may be higher by 25 to 30 per cent than that of the prototype. -There are many aspects to the problem but these cannot be dealt with here.

The lower straight sections of the curves of Fig. IV-11 show the *natural frequency in air*. That of the steel model was 0.63, those of the others deviated from this for different reasons. That of the wooden model deviated because no perfectly rigid clamping could be ensured, and those of the lucite models because of the different internal damping. Nevertheless, the deviation for "dynamically similar elasticity models" remained within ±5 per cent.

96

As for the natural frequencies in still water, two general statements can be made on the basis of the best fitting curves:

1. The *natural frequency proper* decreases with rising water levels since the mass of the system is increased by the added mass of water.

2. The *water mass* excited to oscillate by the vibrating cantilever has its own *natural frequency* to be observed also at the wider, initial vibrations of the cantilever, but is damped less and eventually becomes predominant (Fig. IV-14). In this particular case, natural frequency was lower than that of the cantilever (see the left-side set of curves in Fig. IV-11).

The line of natural frequencies should display an abrupt change in slope at a water level equal to the cantilever bottom. In the figures, this point lies mostly at a higher level. This fact does not imply errors of measurement but that the transition is, instead of being abrupt, a gradual one. And, evidently, there is some scattering as well.

Since there is as yet no acceptable theory available for this transition, it was considered simpler to fit a logarithmic straight line to the rather widely scattered points disregarding thus the fact that in this way the relative height of the change in slope was not the same for the different models.

On the basis of the right-side curves of Fig. IV-11 it can be stated that the best fitting lines of the proper natural frequency in still water are situated in a range within $+12$ to $-18$ per cent around the line of the steel model. The range would probably have been reduced to $+9$ and $-15$ per cent if the correction of the natural frequency in air could have been perfect.

The second "natural" frequency of the cantilever induced by the oscillating water mass falls within a range of similar width to the natural frequency

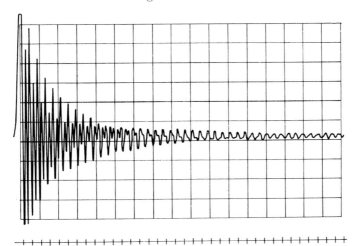

Fig. IV-14. Oscillogram of natural vibration of 1 : 1 model. Below: time signals

proper. The exception to this is the 1 : 16.3 model where an inaccuracy of some tenths of a millimetre in mounting may entail significant effects and, particularly in still water, the capillarity forces could be also relatively large.

The *flow-induced* vibrations also have two principal characteristics: the *flow-induced frequency* $n$ and the *flow-induced double amplitude* $\Delta$.

The variation of the *flow-induced frequencies* follows a trend similar to that of the natural frequencies but the relative frequency values $n/\sqrt{g/d}$ obtained for the different models differ but slightly from each other (Fig. IV-12).

In contrast with the curves $f/\sqrt{g/d}$ determined in still water the break points of the curves $n/\sqrt{g/d}$ are at higher levels, since even for tailwater levels somewhat higher than the lower end of the cantilever the hydrodynamic conditions in the surroundings of the box remain unchanged, the flow being supercritical in this section. Vibrations are maintained permanently because even the free jet impinges upon the box (Fig. IV-1). An arrangement with the bottom of the cantilever at a higher position would probably have been more fortunate, since then the effects on the box would have ceased below a certain tailwater level. Nevertheless, the natural frequency in air occurred at low tailwater levels and was hardly modified by water drops adhering to the box and by the random scatter of measurement data. In the region where the relative flow-induced frequency varied with water depth, the average relative frequencies of the diverse models were within ±10 per cent of the average found for the steel model (considered as prototype). Obviously, this is the error of the absolute prototype frequencies calculated from model data.

The relative double amplitudes, $\Delta/d$ (at any downstream level) varied in a random manner between zero and some maximum value and followed a more or less normal probability distribution. In accordance with this last statement, the maximum amplitudes observed were almost three times as wide as the average amplitudes. This is easy to check in Fig. IV-9 by comparing the peaks of the relative amplitude curves.

Concerning model similitude, it should be noted from Fig. IV-13 that the three larger models showed wider, the two smaller ones narrower relative amplitudes.

No significant differences could be detected between the 1 : 10.2 models of statically and dynamically similar elasticity (this was also true for the flow-induced frequencies). It was for this reason that detailed measurements on the 1 : 4.06 and 1 : 16.3 models of statically similar elasticity, performed otherwise on the 1 : 10.2 model, have been omitted.

The average relative amplitude measurements in the different models will be seen to be distributed over a rather wide zone. As to the maximum relative double amplitude (which is of the greatest importance for practical purposes), the position and magnitude were found to be different in the various models. Concerning the position, the difference is insignificant: in the 1 : 16.3 model the amplitude peak was at $h_d/d = 1.8$; in the 1.58 : 1 model it was at $h_d/d = 2.0$. The relative position of the peak in the 1 : 16.3 model was thus higher by 12 per cent than in the 1.58 : 1 model. The difference was similar for the 1 : 10.2 model, whereas the 1 : 4.06 and the 1 : 1 models produced practically the same values as the 1.58 : 1 "prototype".

On the basis of the foregoing, all models could be considered sufficiently accurate for determining the *position* of the maximum amplitude.

Concerning the *magnitude* of the maximum amplitude, the differences were greater. The maximum relative amplitude obtained from the smallest models was about $\Delta/d = 0.009$, while that from the steel model was about $\Delta/d = 0.017$. This means that if the prototype amplitude is calculated using the data obtained from the smallest models the probable error is about $-47$ per cent, i.e. hardly more than half the actual value is obtained. This difference can be attributed to internal damping, to viscous and capillarity effects, and evidently — though only to a limited extent — to observation and construction errors. Since the magnitude of the amplitudes is usually less important than the position of the maximum amplitude and the corresponding frequency, the result can be considered satisfactory. As mentioned earlier, the models produced excellent results on the frequencies and this is most important for avoiding resonance.

It is concluded that the location of the greatest amplitudes and the corresponding frequency can be determined well and the effect of modifying the natural frequency of the structure (to avoid resonance) can be checked. The error of the amplitude itself, especially if superimposed on a large displacement, can be allowed for by a conservative factor of safety. Thus, the problems arising in practice can be solved with the required accuracy.

After the above investigations with the cantilever in mounting position "a" and vibrational direction perpendicular to axis "0", similar investigations were carried out in the direction perpendicular to axis "1".* Then the whole process was repeated with mounting position "b" in both directions. On the basis of these latter investigations the earlier statements required no modification, neither from a qualitative nor from a quantitative point of view. The deviations observed were smaller than or equal to, those in the case "a"–"0" [83]. Their analysis will therefore be omitted here.

* Results concerning the "in-line" and "cross-flow" oscillations of a similarly mounted cantilever were presented by King [97b] at the Baden-Baden Congress of IAHR, 1977. The present author gave some explanation concerning in-line oscillations ("in longitudinal direction") at the Stockholm Symposium in 1970 [81].

## 2.3 Applicability of the Hydroelastic Similitude Method

In addition to the tests described in the previous subsection there are a few comparative sets of experiments reported in the literature (some of those have already been dealt with in Chapter II). From among these, attention should be paid first of all to the investigations carried out in the Delft Hydraulic Laboratory and at the Hagestein weir [46, 99, 102], in the Leningrad VNIIG Laboratory [2], furthermore in the Älvkarleby Laboratory and on the Kainji dam [26a, 186b].

Our own investigations for verifying the hydroelastic similitude method were accomplished on a structure of angular shape, and thus, the conditions of the investigations closely approximated those of engineering practice and at the same time ensured the opportunity to draw conclusions of fundamental importance.

The experimental investigations have proved the correctness of our similitude method. To sum up, the following qualitative and quantitative statements can be made:

1. By means of the hydroelastic similitude method it is possible to perform hydroelastic investigations on hydraulic structures within the scale limits required for practical purposes.

2. The smallest scale of the models was 1 : 26, but for large structures (with an order of magnitude of several tens of metres) one may safely assume that even more reduced models may be used given that proper care is applied.

3. Although experimental results are affected by the internal damping of the model material, in flowing water this effect on vibration frequencies is very weak.

4. When calculating flow-induced prototype frequencies, an accuracy of ±10 per cent can be expected from the models.

5. Average and peak amplitudes appearing in the prototype in the range of the maximum oscillations may become twice as high as if calculated from model laws.

6. The above statements are valid for all structural materials in use at present for hydraulic model experimentation (wood, metals, lucite, hard PVC, etc.).

Details to be found in the literature do not disprove these statements. The only contradictory statement refers to item 5 since Kolkman has found that relative amplitudes in the model are mostly larger than those observed in the prototype. This observation seems to be realistic mainly for structures where there is a great likelihood of local plate vibrations occurring thereby increasing structural damping to a considerable extent.

100

The present author has had no experience concerning models designed for local plate vibrations. On the other hand, the plates of models reproducing the vibrations of the whole structure are locally absolutely rigid from a practical point of view, therefore the damping due to local plate vibrations is indeed absent. Exceptionally, Kolkman found that the relative amplitude of the prototype was only 30 per cent of that of the model. These experiences show that when evaluating our results in accordance with item 5, we were most certainly conservative. Nevertheless, special care should be devoted to the modelling of the seals, since considerable overdimensioning may easily occur.

Careful modelling of the entrance and exit velocity distributions is called for; this is also true of the side walls because these may have a considerable effect upon the excitation of vibrations.

At very small gate openings, self-controlled vibrations may occur; it is practicable to investigate them using larger-scale slice models.

As for other special details, the reader is referred to the references. Methodological studies may bring new and useful results in the future.

# V. Model Techniques, Instrumentation

So far as model techniques and instrumentation are concerned, only limited information can be given since the literature tends to have little to say in this respect.

## 1. Techniques of Constructing Hydroelastic Models

Model experiments reported in different papers were carried out on *scales* between 1 : 1 [2, 83] and 1 : 70 [95].

The *material* of the models: lucite [83], plexi [187], steel [213], wood [83], hard PVC [122], a hard PVC named "trovidur" [99], synthetic resin reinforced by nylon filaments [60].

Data on *elastic properties* are usually retained. Lean stated [122] that the Young's modulus of his hard PVC was 35400 kp/cm² and its *specific gravity:* 1.35 p/cm³. The present author used, besides the above materials, a Yugoslav plastic called Decelith whose specific gravity was $\gamma_1 = 1.43 \pm$ $\pm$ 0.02 p/cm³, Young's modulus $E_1 = 31400 \pm 2500$ kp/cm², shear modulus $G = 10400 \pm 400$ kp/cm² [71], furthermore, the American lucite with a specific gravity of $\gamma_1 = 1.196$ p/cm³ and Young's modulus $E_1 = 36600 \pm$ $\pm$ 1800 kp/cm² [83].

Young's modulus depends slightly on temperature and frequency; in the case of "trovidur" the deviation is within 7 per cent [99].

The *ballast* applied to complete the mass of elastically similar models is generally brass [60, 71, 83], steel [83] or lead [178]. However, a steel pipe has been modelled in such a way that the PVC model pipe was filled with ammonium sulphate solution to complete the mass [37a].

Virtually no data can be found on how the model elements were assembled. The Dutch probably applied welding because Kolkman mentioned that trovidur was weldable [99]. In the author's investigations steel was generally welded, wood glued and screwed, while both lucite and decelith were glued [71, 83].

Almost certainly the models of the structures were designed by adopting certain simplifications, but about this hardly any reference can be found [83, 99].

In certain experiments the *elastic suspension* was realized by piano strings. Parkins mentions [156] that the suspension was made on a horizontal elastic rod, and by modifying its span the elasticity of the suspension could be

102

varied. There is no information whether or not the rod had any great influence on the mass of the vibrating system. In experiments performed in VITUKI, a stainless resistance wire "W18" was used.

The *sealing* of the prototype structures is either neglected entirely or modelled very carefully because, particularly in a dry state, it considerably modifies the damping.

Kolkman [102] used sealing of limp material supported by steel springs in order to make the rigidity correspond to that in the prototype.

If the effects are not modified by the *deformation* of the structure, a rigid model can be applied [63, 172]. If parts of considerable size of the structure move together, those can be constructed as rigid ones with elastic metal connections whose damping is low. This system is recommended for self-controlled vibrations [172].

Sliding surfaces were modelled by rollers to reduce friction [156].

The low friction of the prototype rollers was realized in the VITUKI laboratory by disproportionately small pin diameters [71].

## 2. Vibrometric Instruments

To measure vibrations in the prototype the Dutch used accelerometers [46], mounted on the vibrating structure. The sensitivity of these instruments was $10^{-5}$ $g$. The signals were recorded by means of a 10-channel tape recorder.

Vibrations in model were measured by means of rigidly mounted inductive transducers [45, 46, 58, 154], strain gauges (Fig. V-1) [2, 75, 83, 156], and other transducers not specified in detail [213]. The signals were generally visualized on an oscilloscope screen and recorded by photography [9, 45, 71]. Kolkman reported details about recording on 10 cm wide paper tape [102]. Hart and Prins investigated natural vibrations using an inductive transducer, D. C. amplifier and some sort of recording instrument [58]. The average amplitude was measured by a separate filter and a voltmeter, while the characteristic amplitude of the envelope by an electron-multiplier and a voltmeter. According to Allersma [9] the measuring range of the inductive transducer is $3 \times 10^{-3}$ to 1 mm. In the experiments performed in the VITUKI laboratory, the so-called "vibromez" head was applied. This will be dealt with in the next section.

Forces were measured with the help of strain gauges [9] and capacitive dynamometers [58].

Pulsating pressures were measured by means of piezoelectric cells [9]. Locher [129] applied an on-line computer and determined characteristic root mean square values.

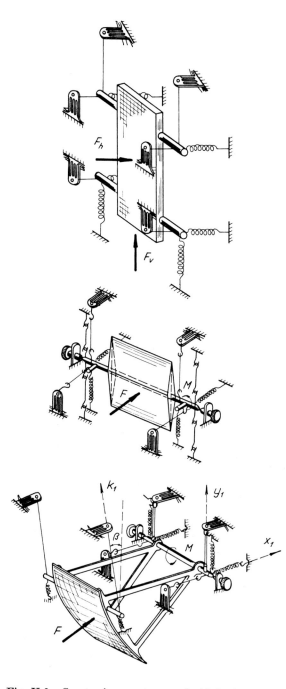

Szeloch [187] used electric resistance measurement (perhaps by strain gauges) to measure unspecified data (probably displacement) and a film camera for recording them from the oscilloscope screen.

In Hungary, at the VITUKI laboratory, the measurement instrumentation is quite up-to-date. One of the vibrometric devices, the "vibromez" head developed at the Instrumentation Section of VITUKI is up to international standards and surpasses in many respects the instruments produced in other countries.

### 3. The Vibrometric Head "Vibromez"

For the measurement of vibrations of hydraulic models (including prototype structures) special waterproof transducers not disturbing the free movement of the structure through mechanical contact are needed. Such an instrument with the appurtenant equipment was developed in accordance with the author's specifications by L. Pálos in the VITUKI laboratories. The experimental specimens of the instrument were used for the tests on the Nagymaros stop-log.

Fig. V-1. Suspension systems of Abelev's gate models

The vibrometric head (Fig. V-2), which has been named "vibromez", is essentially an electronic oscillator whose frequency depends on the distance between its front plate and a nonmagnetic metal plate located before it. The change in frequency is converted into a variation in the voltage output resulting in a deflection of the cathode ray on the screen of the oscilloscope. As long as the distance between the front plate and the metal plate is less than 2 mm, the relationship between the distance and the ray deflection remains a linear one, i.e. on the screen of the oscilloscope a time curve proportional with the displacement is displayed and can be photographed. (There is, of course, no obstacle against manufacturing "vibromez" heads for smaller or larger measurement ranges. It is also possible to produce "vibromez" heads with a diameter of 8 mm instead of the present 2 cm.) Linearity was checked and the calibration line separately determined for each (altogether five) "vibromez" head. The calibration consisted of static and dynamic calibration.

In the course of *static calibration*, the output voltage determined by the distance between the "vibromez" head and the metal plate having varied position (Fig. V-3) was measured by a digital voltmeter (Fig. V-4). From diagrams representing the relationships between distance and voltage (e.g.

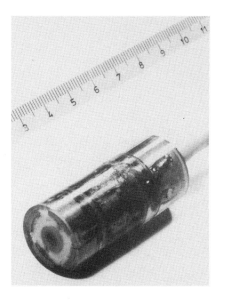

Fig. V-2. "Vibromez" head serving to measure vibrations and displacements of beam. (Centimetre scale is given for comparison)

Fig. V-3. Frame used for static calibration of "vibromez" heads

105

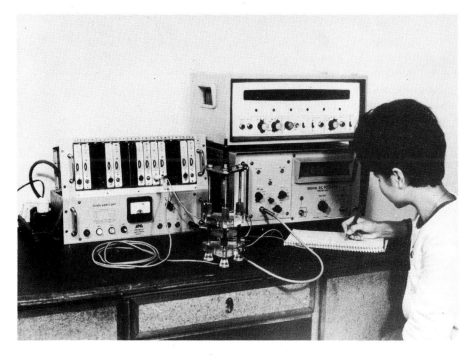

Fig. V-4. Static calibration of "vibromez" heads

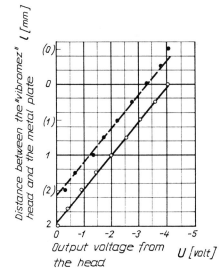

Fig. V-5. Static calibration curves of a "vibromez" head. Continuous line: metal plate parallel with front surface of head. Dotted line: angle between metal plate and front plate is 5°

Fig. V-6. Calibration in situ of "vibromez" heads through a caliper immediately preceding measurement. The number 1.5 on the caliper means that on the metal plate of the caliper a 1.5 mm thick plexi plate is glued. Thus, when in contact with "vibromez" head, the distance between front plate of head and metal plate is precisely 1.5 mm

Fig. V-5) it can be stated that linearity was practically perfect for all of the heads within a range of at least 1.4 (for three heads even 1.6) mm long. Within this section the measurement points deviated from the straight line of best fit by not more than 0.03 mm. The largest deviation experienced within the whole 2 mm long interval from the straight line of best fit was 0.16 mm for one of the heads, 0.1 mm for three heads, and 0.05 mm for one head. Linearity was preserved even when the front plate of the head was in a position oblique at 4 to 5° to the metal plate. The situation was the same if the head was immersed in water of varied temperature.

Fig. V-7. Vibrating plate for dynamic calibration with a "vibromez" head and the electromagnet moving it

The calibration lines were not identical for the different heads nor was this necessary since the deflection of the cathode ray was adjusted separately for each head at each measurement series. In Fig. V-6, the distance caliper is butted to the head. The caliper was a metal plate with a 1.5 mm thick perspex plate on its one side and with a 0.5 mm thick perspex plate on the other. By butting this caliper to the front plate of the "vibromez"

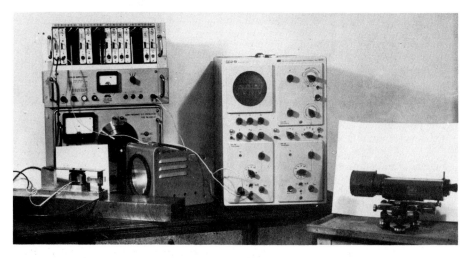

Fig. V-8. Instrument group for dynamic calibration of "vibromez" heads. From left to right: electromagnetic vibrating frame with "vibromez" head; coder; sound frequency generator; stroboscope; oscilloscope; precision level

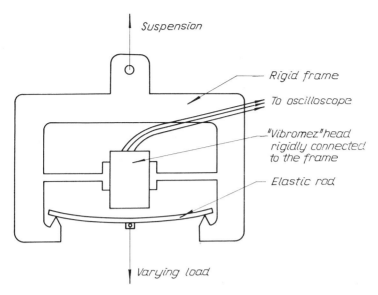

Fig. V-9. Fundamental sketch for force measurement by "vibromez" head

head, the oscilloscope could be adjusted to these two distances between which linearity of all heads was practically perfect. The amplitudes measured generally also remained within this interval, since the "vibromez" heads

in the model were positioned so that the average distance between the front of the head and the respective metal plate on the model should be around 1 mm, i.e. in the middle of the calibration range.

*Dynamic calibration* served to check whether or not the distances, varying in time, were shown correctly by the instrument.

A cantilever plate (Fig. V-7) was excited by means of an electromagnet connected to a sound frequency generator. The frequency was around 20 cps. The displacement of the end of the cantilever plate was measured simultaneously by a statically calibrated "vibromez" head and by levelling (Fig. V-8). Levelling was performed in such a way that the end of

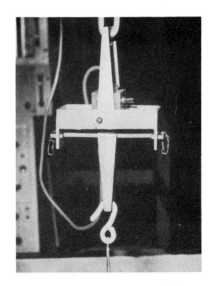

Fig. V-10. "Vibromez" head dynamometer inserted into practically inextensible suspension cable

109

the cantilever plate was illuminated by a stroboscope with a frequency close to that of the vibration. The two extreme positions of the end of the vibrating plate which appeared to move slowly in the field of vision of the levelling instrument were then determined with an accuracy of 0.01 mm.

As a result of dynamic calibration it was ascertained that the difference between the value shown on the oscilloscope and that measured by levelling generally did not exceed 0.05 mm.

The "vibromez" head can also be utilized to measure oscillating forces In the VITUKI laboratory, a gate model was suspended on a light elastic plate as a two-support girder. The elasticity of the plate modelled the elasticity of the prototype suspension because the overdimensioned suspending wires in the model were to be considered inextensible. The "vibromez" head measured the deflection variation of the plate, i.e. force variations proportionate to deflection (Fig. V-9, 10).

# VI. Application Examples

An application example of fundamental significance has been treated in Chapter IV and a few others were mentioned very briefly in Chapter II. Two other model experiments concerning practical problems will be presented with a number of interesting details.

In *Hungary*, hydroelastic model experiments were performed in the hydraulic laboratory of VITUKI in connexion with the first variant of the gate structure of the second Tisza barrage [54, 56], the hinged-leaf gate of the Tass navigation lock [55] (the prototype has already been realized), (the stop-logs designed for the Nagymaros and Kisköre barrages [65, 71] (the prototype has already been realized at the Kisköre barrage), and the turbine gate of the Kisköre Water Power Plant [76] (the prototype has already been realized). Among these, for the investigation of the Nagymaros–Kisköre stop-logs, an elastic stop-log model with elastic suspension was made, while for the others rigid structure models with elastic suspensions were prepared. In this chapter, the investigation of the Nagymaros–Kisköre stop-log will be briefly treated.

Among hydroelastic model experiments performed in *other countries* in connexion with high- and low-head dams and power plants as well as with a great variety of different structures of maritime constructions, the experiments related to the ‘Hagestein weir and carried out on the prototype and on models at the Delft Hydraulic Laboratory mainly by Kolkman will be outlined in this chapter. This experiment series was carried out, among others, on an elastic model structure with elastic suspension in open surface flow. In this respect the investigation ranks among the classical ones.

## 1. Investigation of the Nagymaros—Kisköre Stop-Log [65, 67, 71, 83]

Since these investigations have been described in considerable detail in Ref. [71], only the most important results will be summarized.

The purpose of the investigations was to determine the hydrodynamic forces attacking the stop-logs *lowered into moving water* (Fig. VI-1) when, for some reason, the main gate became unmovable, i.e. not totally closable.

Since the flow was of the open-channel type, flow characteristics were modelled according to the Froude law. From the point of view of elasticity, the model of the structure itself was designed, after preliminary information obtained from Eq. (16), on the basis of Eq. (26). It was then completed

Fig. VI-1. Investigation of 1 : 20 scale model of Nagymaros-Kisköre stop-log in flowing water. Gate structure totally lifted, stop-log slightly submerged

with the necessary ballast according to Eq. (9). An illustration of the model stop-log is shown in Fig. VI-2.

The displacements of the model stop-log were measured at five points (Fig. VI-3): at one of the ends, at one of the suspension points and in the

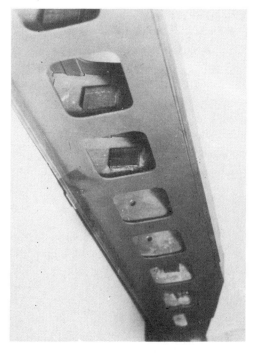

Fig. VI-2. The aluminium ribs in the stop-log model with pieces of brass ballast glued on them, seen from the lower side of stop-log

Fig. VI-3. Model of stop-log with "vibromez" heads and vertical cantilever supporting them for measuring vertical and horizontal vibrations of mid-span cross section. Rubber strings used for vertical and horizontal stretching and one of suspension wires are to be seen. Vertical movement of end and of invisible suspension point of stop-log were also measured by "vibromez" heads

Fig. VI-4. Vertical vibrations of a suspension point (upper curve) and mid-span point (lower curve) of stop-log in flowing water

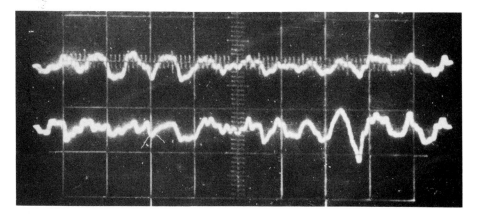

middle of the stop-log the vertical movements, at mid-span at the top and bottom the horizontal movements were observed. The "vibromez" head served to perceive the displacements being capable, without any mechanical contact, of transmitting to the oscilloscope screen those movements not exceeding 2 millimetres of the non-magnetic metal plate glued to the surface of the stop-log model. Figure VI-4 shows the vertical vibrations of the beam in flowing water.

Basic tests to determine the natural frequency in air and still water were also carried out with this model. The vibration in air can be well approximated by certain simplified *mathematical models*, and thus the correctness of the elastic model design could be checked. Since in this respect the results were very favourable, the same confidence was placed on the other parts of the investigations — for which no mathematical treatment is available at present.

From among the measurement results it should be recalled only that the beam itself proved to be highly overdimensioned for flexural effects since the cross section was designed to bear a one-side hydrostatic load. This means that when oscillating on the suspension cables the beam behaved almost like a rigid body. According to the measurements the flexural vibrations were completely insignificant in both horizontal and vertical directions. Torsional vibrations were also negligible.

When dimensioning the suspension cable, vertical movements of the beam were the critical factor of the design. Since the vertical displacement

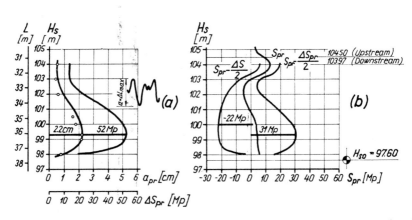

Fig. VI-5. Vertical movements of and vertical hydrodynamic load on stop-log in a 6000 m³/s flood (through the opening studied, discharge was about 600 m³/s) ;(a) maximum oscillation amplitudes $a_{pr}$ of a suspension point and the force oscillation amplitudes $\Delta S_{pr}$ in two cables together calculated therefrom; (b) average load $S_{pr}$ on two suspension cables of stop-log and its extreme values due to vibration. $H_s$ = position of the top of stop-log above sea level, $H_{so}$ = lowest position of the top of the stop-log when its lower edge attains the bottom, $L$ = length of suspension cable of the stop-log

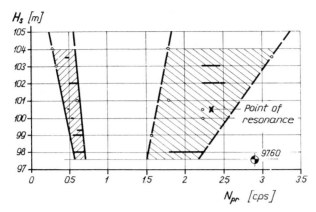

Fig. VI-6. Primary (excited) and secondary (resonant) vibrations of suspension point of stop-log in 6000 m³/s flood

of the beam was equal to the elongation of the cable, the cable force was to be calculated therefrom. Figure VI-5a shows the largest elongation amplitude and the largest change $\Delta S_{pr}$ of the cable force resulting therefrom. The mean cable force $S_{pr}$ caused by hydrodynamic effects was determined in an earlier experiment [63]. The extreme values of the hydrodynamic cable force were approximated as $S_{pr} \pm \dfrac{\Delta S_{pr}^{\bullet}}{2}$ (Fig. VI-5b). The total load on the cable was obtained by the addition of the underwater weight of the beam. For the stop-log tested this sum was always positive, though in the case of a 6000 m³/s flood it was near zero. If it had been negative, it would have been necessary to increase the weight of the beam or to improve its form in order to create better streamflow conditions, otherwise the beam would have floated upwards.

The vertical vibrations of the stop-log were also interesting because of the two frequency zones to be distinguished (Fig. VI-6). The slower vibrations were excited by the flow but secondarily also quicker vibrations appeared near the resonance frequency. The amplitudes of the latter were considerably smaller than those of the excited vibrations. The "resonance point" indicated in the diagram is the result of the investigation in still water.

## 2. Investigation of the Hagestein Barrage [45, 46, 99, 100, 102]

The Hagestein "visor" gate has already been shown in Fig. II-13. Figure VI-7 displays the plan, a side view and a cross section with a few important dimensions.

115

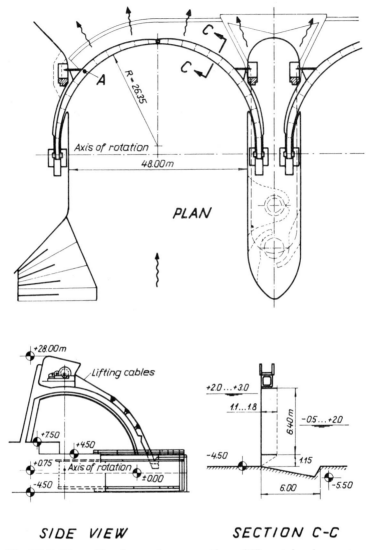

PLAN

SIDE VIEW          SECTION C-C

Fig. VI-7. Plan, side view and cross section of Hagestein visor gate

The extraordinarily slender gate structure, acting like a half-ring subject to tensile stresses, bears the hydraulic pressure attacking on the concave side and it can be excited to vibrate when opened partially. The researchers of the Delft Laboratory, primarily Kolkman, created artificially excited vidrations on the prototype (in a dry construction pit, then in the construction pit inundated in still water, finally in flowing water), the same tests were also carried out in the laboratory on a 1 : 20 hydroelastically similar

116

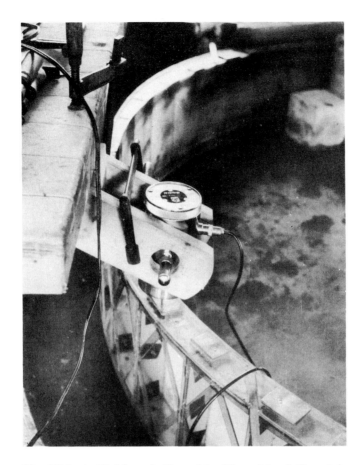

Fig. VI-8. Artificial excitation of 1 : 20 model of Hagestein visor gate model under dry conditions (Courtesy Delft Hydraulic Laboratory, The Netherlands)

three-dimensional scale model (Fig. VI-8) and on a 1 : 6 scale sectional model. The principles of modelling were the same as those treated in Chapter III: the Froude law was accepted, in the large model the total elasticity of the structure, and in the sectional model the elasticity of the suspension was adjusted to that law.

The prototype was excited by a "hydraulic pulsator" with a maximum force amplitude of $10^5$ N, between frequencies 0 and 10 Hz. The force was concentrated in the middle of the gate span. The direction of the force was horizontal–radial, horizontal–tangential and vertical. The movement of the gate was measured by inductive displacement transducers and accelerometers above the water surface.

117

Fig. VI-9. 1 : 20 Hagestein gate model in operation (Courtesy Delft Hydraulic Laboratory, The Netherlands)

In the model, inductive displacement transducers were applied but because of insulation problems, only one of them was mounted under water. Strain gauges were not used because they would have influenced the movement of the slim structure. The movement of the structure was measured at as many points as was necessary to calculate the internal stresses. The displacements of the structure only attained one tenth of that permissible without danger.

The flow-induced vibrations of the 48 m span gate were between 0.6 to 1.5 Hz (cps) with amplitudes and frequencies of random character. The measurements were performed at four gate lifting positions (Fig. VI-9) and normally a low-frequency vibration and often also another super-imposed vibration with small amplitudes and resonant frequency were experienced. The higher frequencies, observed rarely, were very weak.

Figure VI-10 shows the displacement maxima created by the artificial exciting forces of different frequencies related to unit force at the middle of the gate directly measured on the prototype and those converted from the model to the prototype. The explanation of the various parts of the figure is in the following table:

118

Fig. VI-10. Relative displacement maxima [metre/Newton] of middle hinge of Hagestein gate structure vs. frequency of exciting force

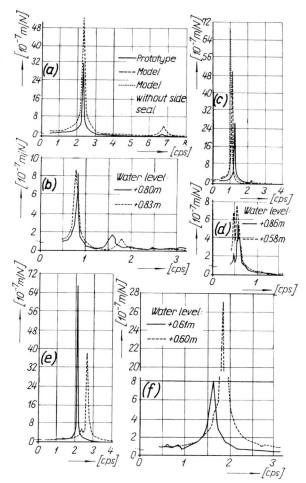

| Part | Direction of excitation and measured vibrations | Medium |
|------|--------------------------------------------------|--------------|
| a | horizontal–radial | air |
| b | horizontal–radial | still water |
| c | horizontal–tangential | air |
| d | horizontal–tangential | still water |
| e | vertical | air |
| | vertical | still water |

119

It can be seen in the parts of its figure that for resonance frequencies the model deviates only slightly from the prototype but the discrepancy between the corresponding amplitudes, as pointed out already, is somewhat more significant.

Satisfactory results were obtained from the investigations concerning operating conditions.

# VII. Future of Hydroelastic Modelling

For determining the vibrations of hydraulic structures by means of model experiments, the method treated in this book offers a generally satisfactory basis from the *theoretical* point of view. Exceptions are cases when the fluid cannot be considered incompressible. Such are the phenomena of water hammer and cavitation and a substantial group of flows with an air phase.

This does not mean that by studying thoroughly the individual problem, the conditions of modelling cannot be established but for treatment of more general validity, further research is required. On the other hand, an improvement of modelling methods (the similitude theory) is likely to be achieved by involving theorems of energy transport processes.

From the point of view of *practical model construction,* difficulties arise when the location of origin of the vibration is geometrically small in comparison with the whole vibrating structure and the flow space affecting the phenomenon. In such cases the most essential structural details cannot be modelled since the available space in a laboratory is insufficient to provide an acceptable scale. The problems in connexion with structural friction, sealing (Fig. VII-1), and local plate vibrations belong to this sphere of prob-

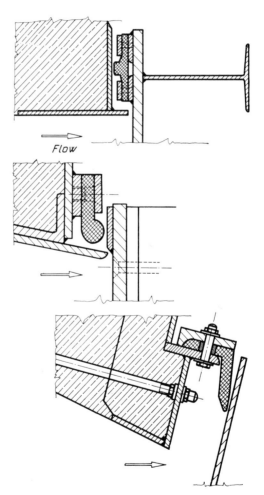

Fig. VII-1. Modelling seals is often a most difficult task

lems. Modelling or the possibility of modelling fall within the scope of problems requiring further studies.

As for *measurement techniques*, a number of new instruments need to be put into regular use. In industrially highly developed countries, this problem is a minor one, or one that has already been solved, but in other countries much still remains to be done.

The further miniaturization of displacement and pressure transducers, their simultaneous serial application, the direct transfer of their signals to computer data carriers is an indispensable condition for a more detailed revelation of phenomena.

A detailed study of the velocity field around the structure is also necessary to enable the improvement of streamflow conditions. This calls for velocity measuring devices which do not disturb the flow. In this respect, at least under laboratory conditions, the increasing application of laser techniques should be considered.

The use of vibratory devices ought to become more general since the application of arbitrary exciting forces helps to give a better picture of the vibrational properties of structures.

There seems to be a lack of published data on the *comparison* of model and prototype measurements concerning hydroelastic vibrations. It is necessary to perform systematic and regular follow-up measurements on prototypes. The data of these checks need to be published or at least communicated to the model investigator.

Development is in progress towards a further slenderizing of pier structures. Thus, in the future these will no longer be able to be considered rigid. Even so, their elastic modelling, based on the criteria treated in this book, will not entail any particular difficulty.

One of the most difficult problems for the designer is to take into account the "added mass" of water. Were the added mass known, the model experiment could in many cases be avoided if the danger of resonance is the only question. It appears to be necessary to carry out systematic experiments to determine the added mass of structures and cross-sections frequently encountered in practice.

It can be mentioned, that the experimental chambers with controllable air pressure, which were built recently and which serve first of all the model investigation of the cavitation of ship propellers under natural manœuvering conditions, can amplify the possibilities also for hydroelastic model investigations. Viz. in the performance of the phenomena the elasticity of the air plays a not negligible role or if one must calculate with the occurrence of cavitation, the solution might be to put the model inside a room with low air pressure.

Model experimentation is an expensive means and should be applied only if theoretical calculation methods are inadequate to solve the problem. We have also to consider the possibility that future theoretical methods will not keep pace with the new problems arising and thus, not only will modelling remain necessary but its methods and its special theoretical approach have also to be developed. Through this book the author has attempted to make a modest step in that direction.

# VIII. References

[1] Aartsen, M. A.–Venis, W. A.: Model Investigations on Wave Attack on Structures. VIIIth IAHR Congress, Montreal, 1959.

[2] Abelev, A. S.: Investigations of the Total Pulsating Hydrodynamic Load Acting on Bottom Outlet Sliding Gates and its Scale Modelling. VIIIth IAHR Congress, Montreal, 1959.

[3] Abelev, A. S.: Pulsations of Hydrodynamic Loads Acting on Bottom Gates of Hydraulic Structures and their Calculation Methods. Xth IAHR Congress, London, 1963.

[4] Abelev, A. S.–Dolnikov, L. L.: Investigation of Non-Stationary Hydrodynamic Forces. Induced by a Plate Oscillating in Liquid Flow (Two-Dimensional Problem), XIVth IAHR Congress, Paris, 1971.

[5] Abelev, A. S.–Dolnikov, L. L.: Auto-Oscillations of High-Head Flat Gates of Hydraulic Structures and Preventive Measures against Them. IAHR Symposium, Stockholm, 1970.

[5a] Abelev, A. S.—Dolnikov, L. L.—Vilin, G. V.: On Dynamic Criterion for Vertical-Lift Sluice Gates Considering Hydrodynamic Damping. XVIIth IAHR Congress, Baden-Baden, 1977.

[6] Abelev, A. S.–Solnyshkov, V. A.: Investigation of Actual Hydrodynamic Loads on Bottom Gates of Hydraulic Structures. XIth IAHR Congress, Leningrad, 1965.

[6a] Abramson, H. N.: Hydrofoil Flutter; Some Recent Developments. IUTAM–IAHR Symposium, Karlsruhe, 1972.

[7] Ackermann, H.: Schwingungen an unter- und überströmten Wehren und ihre Beseitigung. Der Bauingenieur, Heft 9, 1962.

[7a] Adam, U.–Sturtzel, W.: Ermittlung der Festigkeitsbeanspruchung langer Schiffe mit geringer Seitenhöhe unter Einwirkung statischer und dynamischer Kräfte mit Hilfe eines Gliedermodells. Schiff und Hafen, 1974, Heft 5, 26. Jahrgang.

[8] Agroszkin–Dmitrijev–Pikalov: Hidraulika (Hydraulics). (Trans. from Russian.) Tankönyvkiadó, Budapest, 1952.

[9] Allersma, E.: The Virtual-Mass of a Submerged Sluice Gate. VIIIth IAHR Congress, Montreal, 1959.

[10] Alonso, M.–Finn, E. J.: Fundamental University Physics, Addison-Wesley, Reading, Don Mills, Palo Alto, London, 1967.

[11] Angelin, S.: Hydraulic Studies of Gates and Shafts to a Diversion Tunnel. VIIIth IAHR Congress, Montreal, 1959.

[12] Angelin, S.–Flagestad, K.: Vibration of Arched Stop-Logs Immersed in Streaming Water. IAHR IXth Congress, Dubrovnik, 1961.

[13] Appel, D. W.–Ch. Stanford–Uppal, H.: Vibration Problems in Hydraulic Structures. Proc. ASCE. HY. November, 1961.

[14] Архангородский, А. Г.–Беленкий, Л. М.: Моделирование прочности судовых конструкций (Modelling of Strength of Naval Structures). Изд. Судостроение, Ленинград, 1969.

[15] Ball, W.: Cavitation and Vibration Studies for a Cylinder Gate Designed for High Heads. VIIIth IAHR Congress, Montreal, 1959.

[16] Ballou, Ch. L.: Investigation of the Wake Behind a Cylinder at Coincidence of a Natural Frequency of Vibration of the Cylinder and the Vortex Shedding Frequency. Technical Report No. 76028-2, Engineering Projects Laboratory. Massachusetts Institute of Technology, Cambridge, Massachusetts, 1967.

[17] Бархатов, А. Н.: Моделирование распространения звука в море (Modelling of Sound Propagation in the Sea). Гидрометеиздат, Ленинград, 1968.

[18] Bishop, R. E. D.: Vibration. Cambridge University Press, London., 1965.

[19] Bogárdi, J.: Vizfolyások hordalékszállítása (Sediment Transport in Rivers). Akadémiai Kiadó, Budapest, 1971.

[20] Bosznay, Á.: Műszaki rezgéstan (Theory of Vibrations in Techniques). Műszaki Könyvkiadó, Budapest, 1962.

[21] Budó, Á.–Pócza, J.: Kísérleti fizika (Experimental Physics). Tankönyvkiadó, Budapest, 1962.

[22] Budó, Á.: Mechanika (Mechanics). Tankönyvkiadó, Budapest, 1965.

[23] Burciu, Alexandru: Determinarea criteriilor de similitudine in modelarea structurala a barajelor de beton. Hidrotechnica, V. 15, Nr. 3, 1970.

[24] Campbell, F. B.: Vibration Problems in Hydraulic Structures. Proc. ASCE HY2, March, 1961.

[25] Cholnoky, T.: Rugalmasságtan I.–II. rész (Theory of Elasticity I–II). University lecture notes Nos. J9-521 and J9-521/a, MTI, Budapest, 1969.

[26] Chon-Chen, Wu.–Landweber, L.: Added Mass of Ogival Cylinders Oscillating Horizontally in a Free Surface. Schiffstechnik Bd. 7., Heft 37, 1960.

[26a] Coxon, R. E.–Angelin, S. V.–Wardle, D. G.: Stoplog Closure–Model Prototype Correlation. Journal of the Hydraulics Division, ASCE, Vol. 99, HY2, February, 1973.

[27] Crandall, S. H.: Random Vibration 1–2. MIT, Cambridge, Mass. 1963.

[28] Daubert, A.: Efforts instationnaires sur des structures immergées en mouvement en vibration (rapport général). XIVth IAHR Congress, Paris, 1971.

[29] Delleur, J. W.–Toebes, G. H.–Liu, L.: Turbulence Measurement in Liquids: Some Considerations and Experiences Regarding Optimisation. Advances in Hot-Wire Anemometry, Int. Symp. Hot-Wire Anemometry. University of Maryland, March, 1967.

[30] Den Hartog, J. P.: Mechanical Vibrations. McGraw-Hill, New York, 1956 (4th edition).

[31] Dirkzwager, M.–Prins, J. E.: Tangential Forces Exerted on Segment Gates, in Partially Raised Positions, by Underflow and Waves. VIIIth IAHR Congress, Montreal, 1959.

[32] Eagleson, P. S., Daily, J. W.: The Effect of Boundary Layer Thickness and Vibrational Amplitude on the Strouhal Number for Flat Plates. Xth IAHR Congress, London, 1963.

[33] Eagleson, P. S.–Shack, W. J.: Maximum Negative Damping in the Flutter of Flat Plates in Water. XIth IAHR Congress, Leningrad, 1965.

[34] Eisenberg, Ph.–Whicker, L. F.: Large Elastic Bending of Cantilever with Hydrodynamic Loading. (Manuscript.)

[35] Elder, R. A.–Garrison, J. M.: Model-Prototype Force Comparisons for Multiple-Leaf Control Gates. XIth IAHR Congress, Leningrad, 1965.

**125**

[36] Elder, R. A.–Hecker, G. E.: Vibration of Reverse Flow Tainter Lock Valves. XIth IAHR Congress, Leningrad, 1965.

[37] Elder, R. A.: Model-Prototype Turbulence Scaling. IXth IAHR Congress, Dubrovnik, 1961.

[37a] Every, M. T.—Prosser, M. T.: Hydroelastic Model Tests of Tripod Structures. XVIIth IAHR Congress, Baden-Baden, 1977.

[38] Escande, L.: Recherches sur le fonctionnement simultané des barrages mobiles en déversoirs et vannes de fond. La Houille Blanche, Nr. spécial B. **728,** 1948.

[39] Fáy, Gy.–Zselev, B.: A hasonlóságelmélet alkalmazása transzportfolyamatok vizsgálatában (Application of Similitude Theory for Studying Transport Processes). MTA Műsz. Tud. Oszt. Közleményei, **33**/1964.

[40] Fortier, A.: Considérations générales sur les problèmes d'aéro- et d'hydro-élasticité. La Houille Blanche, **5,** 1971.

[41] Franke, P. G.–Valentin, F.: Amplitude-Dependent Frequency of an Oscillating Cylinder in a High Velocity Flow. XIVth IAHR Congress, Paris, 1971.

[42] Fritzler, G. L.–Laird, A. D. K.: Hydroelastic Vibrations of Circular Cylinders. Report No. HPS-64-2, Institute of Engineering Research, University of California, Berkeley, California, August, 1964.

[43] Füzy, O.: Vízgépek (Hydraulic Machinery). Tankönyvkiadó, Budapest, 1958.

[44] Gál, A.: Bestimmung der mitschwingenden Wassermasse bei überströmten Fischbauchklappen mit kreiszylindrischem Staublech. Doctoral Dissertation, Stuttgart, 1970.

[45] Geleedst, M.: Elastic Similarity of Models of Structures. Xth IAHR Congress, London, 1963.

[46] Geleedst, M.–Kolkman, P. A.: Comparative Vibration Measurements on the Prototype and the Elastically Similar Model of the Hagestein Weir under Flow Conditions. XIth IAHR Congress, Leningrad, 1965.

[47] Gershunov, E. M.–Leontjev, N. N.–Pashkov, N. N.–Rosanov, N. P.: Investigation of the Problems Concerning Vibration of High Spillway Arch Dam. XIth IAHR Congress, Leningrad, 1965.

[48] Goldrick, R. T.: Ship Vibration. Department of the Navy, David Taylor Model Basin, Report 1451, Dec. 1960.

[49] Grčić, J.: Critical Water-Depth for Hydrodynamic Induced Oscillation of Cantilevered Cylinders. XIVth IAHR Congress, Paris, 1971.

[50] Grein, H.–Pirchl, H.: The Butterfly Valve Used as Damper in Pumped Storage Tailwater Systems. IAHR Symposium, Stockholm, 1970.

[51] Gruber, J.–Blahó, M.: Folyadékok mechanikája (Fluid Mechanics). Tankönyvkiadó, Budapest, 1956.

[52] Grzywienski, A.: Hydraulic Forces on Vertical-Lift Gates. VIIIth IAHR Congress, Montreal, 1959.

[53] Grzywienski, A.: The Effect of Turbulent Flow on Multisection Vertical-Lift Gates. IAHR IXth Congress, Dubrovnik, 1961.

[54] Győrke, O.: A Tiszaburai vízlépcső duzzasztóműve gáttábláinak és utófenekének vizsgálata. Összefoglaló jelentés (Investigation of the Gates and Stilling Basins of the Tiszabura Barrage. Closing report). Budapest, 1959. (Manuscript at the VITUKI Library.)

[55] Győrke, O.: A tassi hajózsilip billenőtáblájával kapcsolatos kismintavizsgálatok. Összefoglaló jelentés (Scale Model Studies Concerning the Hinged Leaf of the

Tass Navigation Lock. Closing Report). Budapest, 1962. (Manuscript at the VITUKI Library.)

[56] Győrke, O.: A tiszaburai vízlépcső gáttábláinak és utófenekének kisminta-vizsgálata (Scale Model Study of the Gates and Stilling Basin of the Tiszabura Barrage). Beszámoló a Vízgazdálkodási Tudományos Kutató Intézet 1959. évi munkájáról, OVF, Budapest, 1962.

[57] Hankó, Z.: Hajózsilip töltésének és ürítésének vizsgálata (Investigation of Filling and Emptying of a Navigation Lock). Mélyépítéstudományi Szemle, **11–12,** 1951.

[57a] Hardwick, J. D.: Flow-Induced Vibration of Vertical-Lift Gate. Journal of the Hydraulics Division, ASCE, May 1974.

[58] Hart, R.–Prins, J. E.: Studies on the Interaction between Turbulent Pressure Fluctuations and Movements of a Structure. VIIIth IAHR Congress, Montreal, 1959.

[59] Hartlen, R. T.–Baines, W. D.–Curril, I. G.: Vortex-Excited Oscillations of a Circular Cylinder. UT Mech E TP 6809, University of Toronto, Canada, Nov. 1968.

[60] Harrison, A. J. M.: Model Study of Siphon Vibrations. XIth IAHR Congress, Leningrad, 1965.

[61] Haszpra, O.: Hidromechanika (Hydromechanics). University lecture note No. J. 9-727. Tankönyvkiadó, Budapest, 1966.

[62] Haszpra, O.: A nagymarosi betétgerenda rezgéstani kismintavizsgálatának elméleti megalapozása. Előadás a Vízgazdálkodási Tudományos Kutató Intézet Hidromechanikai Főosztályán (Theoretical Foundation of the Scale Model Investigation of the Nagymaros Stop-Log. Lecture at the Hydromechanics Department of VITUKI). Budapest, September, 1964.

[63] Haszpra, O.: A nagymarosi vízlépcső duzzasztóműve gáttábláinak, utófenekének és betétgerendáinak hidraulikai kismintavizsgálata. Összefoglaló jelentés (Hydraulic Model Investigation of the Gate, Stilling Basin and Stop-Log of the Nagymaros Barrage. Closing Report). Budapest, 1965. (Manuscript at the VITUKI Library.)

[63a] Haszpra, O.: A hidroelasztikai hasonlóság és alkalmazásai (Hydroelastic Similitude and Its Applications), VITUKI Szemle, June, 1972.

[64] Haszpra, O.: Vízépítési szerkezetek rezgéstani kismintavizsgálatának elméleti alapjai (Theoretical Foundations of Hydroelastic Scale Modelling of Hydraulic Structures). (Lecture at the Hungarian Hydrological Society, 6th April, 1965.) Hidrológiai Közlöny, **9,** 1965.

[65] Haszpra, O.: A Nagymarosi Vízlépcső egy betétgerendájának rezgéstani kis-mintavizsgálata. Összefoglaló jelentés (Model Experiments on the Vibrations of the Nagymaros Stop-Log. Closing Report). (Lecture at the Hydromechanics Department of VITUKI, Budapest, 5th November, 1964.) Budapest, 1966. Manuscript at the VITUKI Library.

[66] Haszpra, O.: Vízépítési szerkezetek rezgéstani kismintavizsgálata. Irodalom-feltárás. Összefoglaló jelentés (Hydroelastic Model Investigation of Hydraulic Structures. Literature Review. Budapest, 1966. (Manuscript at the VITUKI Library.).

[67] Haszpra, O.–Győrke, O.: Erőtani kismintavizsgálatok módszerei (Methods of Dynamic Model Investigations). Beszámoló a Vízgazdálkodási Tudományos Kutató Intézet 1966. évi munkájáról. VITUKI, Budapest, 1968.

[68] Haszpra, O.: Hajlító, nyújtó és csavaró rezgésekre igénybevett vízépítési szerkezetek kismintavizsgálatának néhány elméleti kérdése (Some Theoretical Problems of Model Investigation of Hydraulic Structures Suffering Flexural, Elongational and Torsional Vibrations). Hidrológiai Közlöny, **7,** 1968.

[69] Haszpra, O.: A hidraulikai rezgéstani kismintavizsgálatok jelenlegi állása a Nemzetközi Hidraulikai Kutatásügyi Szövetség Kongresszusainak tükrében (Present State of Hydroelastic Model Experimentation in the Mirror of the Congresses of IAHR). (Manuscript 1967.)

[70] Haszpra, O.: Beszámoló jelentés Dr. Haszpra Ottó C. Sc. tudományos tanácsadó Ford ösztöndíjas tanulmányútjáról (Report on the Ford Fellowship Study Tour of dr. Ottó Haszpra C. Sc., Scientific Consultant). Budapest, 1969. (Manuscript No. 635/188/3 at the VITUKI Library.)

[71] Haszpra, O.: Hidraulikai rezgéstani vizsgálatok betétgerenda rugalmas kismintáján (Hydroelastic Model Investigations on the Elastic Model of a Stop-Log). Hidrológiai Közlöny, **2–3,** 1970.

[72] Haszpra, O.: Accuracy of Model-Prototype Relationships of Flow-Induced Vibrations, (Manuscript.) 1972.

[73] Haszpra, O.: Hidraulikai rezgéstani jelenségek kismintavizsgálata. Összefoglaló jelentés a VITUKI tanulmánytárában (Model Investigation of Hydroelastic Phenomena. Closing Report). Budapest, 1971. (Manuscript at the VITUKI Library.)

[74] Haszpra, O.: Szerkezeti rezgések modellezése a hidraulikában (Modelling of Structural Vibrations in Hydromechanics). Lecture at the National IUTAM Preconference, Miskolc, 1971.

[75] Haszpra, O.: A hidroelasztikai modellezési elmélet kísérleti ellenőrzése (Experimental Checking of the Hydroelastic Similitude Theory), Hidrológiai Közlöny, **9,** 1972.

[75a] Haszpra, O.: Contribution to Subject C (Flow-Induced Structural Vibrations). IAHR-IUTAM Symposium, Karlsruhe, 1972.

[75b] Haszpra, O.: A hidroelasztika modellezési kérdései. Áramláskeltette szerkezeti rezgések kismintavizsgálatának megbízhatósága (Modelling Problems in Hydroelasticity. Reliability of Model Investigations of Flow-Induced Structural Vibrations). Publication of VITUKI Tudományos Napok, Budapest, 1972.

[76] Haszpra, O.: Vízépítési szerkezetek rezgéseinek modellezése. Elmélet, kísérleti igazolás, alkalmazások (Modelling the Vibrations of Hydraulic Structures. Theory, Experimental Verification, Applications). Beszámoló A VITUKI 1971. évi munkájáról. VITUKI, Budapest, 1974.

[77] Haszpra, O.: Theory and Applications of Hydroelastic Modelling. Lecture at universities and research institutes in Iowa City, Vicksburg, Norris, Lafayette, Denver, Fort Collins, Mexico City, Pasadena, Berkeley, Honolulu, Sydney, Cooma, Poona, Addis Ababa, Vienna, during 1968/69.

[78] Haszpra, O.: Hydroelastic Experiments on a Stop-Log Model of a River Barrage. IAHR Symposium, Sockholm, 1970.

[79] Haszpra, O.–Pálos, L.: "Vibromez": un cabezal vibrométrico para investigaciones sobre modelos hidroelásticos. (Manuscript.) Budapest, 1970.

[80] Haszpra, O.: Verificación experimental de la teoría de la semejanza hidroelástica. V Congreso Latinoamericano de Hidráulica, Lima, 1972.

[81] Haszpra, O.: Discussion. Hydroelastic Experiments on a Stop-Log Model of a River Barrage. IAHR Symposium, Stockholm, 1970.

[82] Haszpra, O.: Discussion. To the General Report of Prof. Toebes. XIVth IAHR Congress, Paris, 1971.

[83] Haszpra, O.: Verification of Hydroelastic Similitude criteria. Journal of the Hydraulic Division, ASCE, April, 1976.

[83a] Haszpra, O.: A hidroelasztikai hasonlóságelmélet és kísérleti igazolása. Alkalmazás a vízépítési modellkísérletezésben. (Hydroelastic Similitude Theory and Its Experimental Verification. Application in Hydrotechnical Model Experimentation). Tanulmányok és Kutatási Eredmények 44. szám. VITUKI, Budapest, 1974.

[83b] Haszpra, O.: Hydroelastic Similitude Theory and Its Experimental Verification. Application in Hydrotechnical Model Experimentation. (Doctoral Dissertation). Publication in Foreign Languages, No. 11. VITUKI, Budapest, 1975.

[83c] Haszpra, O.: Modeleksperimentoj kiel modernaj helpiloj de la hidroteknika planado. Sciencaj Komunikaĵoj, Budapest, Julio, 1975.

[83d] Haszpra, O.: Teorio de la hidroelastika simileco kaj ĝia eksperimenta pruvo. Sciencaj Komunikaĵoj, Budapest, Julio, 1976.

[84] Hecker, E.: Hydrodynamic Forces on a Multiple-Leaf Gate-System. XIth IAHR Congress, Leningrad, 1965.

[85] Hecker, G. E.–Elder, R. A.: Hydrodynamic Forces on Single Intake Gates. XIVth IAHR Congress, Paris, 1971.

[86] Hecker, G. E.–Elder, R. A.: Design and Testing of the Nickajack Multileaf Gate System. IAHR Symposium, Stockholm, 1970.

[87] Heller, S. R. Jr.: Hydroelasticity. Chow, Ven Te ed.: Advances in Hydroscience. Vol. 1. Academic Press. New York—London, 1964.

[88] Hellström, B.: Hydraulics of a Submersible Tainter Gate at Bagedeforsen, Sweden, VIIIth IAHR Congress, Montreal, 1959.

[88a] Hino, M.–Kaneko, D.: Interaction between an Oscillating Plate and Shedding Vortices.

[88b] Hoppe, K. G.: Scale Effects in Manœuvring Tests with Small Ship Models. Schiff und Hafen, Heft 5, 1974.

[89] Horeni, P.: Hydraulic Downpull Increase at a Dam Gate Caused by Hydrodynamic Forces. XIVth IAHR Congress, Paris, 1971.

[90] Horváth, I.: A hasonlóságról (On Similitude). Építés és Közlekedéstudományi Közlemények, VII/1–2, 1963.

[91] Hutton, S. I.: Scale Effects. General report of Session D, IAHR Symposium, Stockholm, 1970.

[92] Ippen, A. T.–Toebes, G. H.–Eagleson, P. S.: The Hydroelastic Behavior of Flat Plates as Influenced by Trailing Edge Geometry. Technical Report No. 36. MIT Hydrodynamics Lab., April, 1960.

[93] Ivicsics, L.: Vízépítési kismintavizsgálatok (Hydraulic Model Experiments). OVF. Budapest, 1962.

[94] Jones, W. P.: Manual on Aeroelasticity. North Atlantic Treaty Organisation Advisory Group for Aeronautical Research and Development. NATO, 1959(?).

[95] Karaki, S.–Luecker, A. R.–Cleveland, J.–Mercer, A. G.: High head radial gate seals. A hydraulic model study. IAHR Symposium, Stockholm, 1970.

[96] Kemény, S.: Hajók rezgései (Vibrations of Ships). MTI, Budapest, 1953.

[97] Kennedy, J. F.: Research Activity of the Iowa Institute of Hydraulic Research in 1968. (Manuscript.)

129

[97a] King, R.: Hydroelastic Models and Offshore Design. Civil Engineering, October, 1974.

[97b] King, R.: Vortex-Excited Oscillations of a Cylinder Dipping into Water. XVIIth IAHR Congress, Baden-Baden, 1977.

[98] Кирпичев, М. В.: Теория подобия. (Theory of Similitude). Изд АН СССР, Москва, 1953.

[99] Kolkman, P. A.: Vibration Tests in a Model of a Weir with Elastic Similarity on the Froude Scale. VIIIth IAHR Congress, Montreal, 1959.

[100] Kolkman, P. A.: Vibrations des vannes en positions partiellement montées du barrage de Hagestein. Société Hydrotechnique de France. VIIIèmes Journées de l'Hydraulique, Lille, 1964.

[101] Kolkman, P. A.: Models with Elastic Similarity for the Investigation of Hydraulic Structures. Delft Hydraulics Laboratory, Publication No. 49. July, 1970.

[102] Kolkman, P. A.: Analysis of Vibration Measurements on an Underflow Type of Gate. Xth IAHR Congress, London, 1963.

[103] Kolkman, P. A.: Analysis of Vibration and Damping Measurements on a Reversed Tainter Valve. IAHR Symposium, Stockholm, 1970.

[104] Kolkman, P. A.: Elastisch gelijk vormige modellen van waterbouwkundige constructies, Leergang "Modellen en schaalregels". Delft, 1966.

[105] Kolkman, P. A.: Discussion. The Necessity of Allowing for the Reech-Froude Condition in the Similarity of Turbulent Hydro-Elastic Phenomena. Journal of Hydraulic Research, Vol. 10, No. 1, 1972.

[105a] Kolkman, P. A.: Flow-Induced Gate Vibrations. Delft Hydraulics Laboratory Publications No. 164. Delft, 1976.

[105b] Kolkman, P. A.—Vrijer, A.: Gate Edge Suction as a Cause of Self-Exciting Vibrations. XVIIth IAHR Congress, Baden-Baden, 1977.

[105c] Kolkman, P. A.: Self-Excited Gate Vibrations. XVIIth IAHR Congress, Baden-Baden, 1977.

[106] Kollár, L.: Magas épitmények rezgései a szél hatására (Wind-Induced Vibrations of High Buildings). University lecture note No. 70-1241, MTI, Budapest, 1970.

[107] Korányi, I.: Stabilitáselmélet (Theory of Stability). Lecture Note No. J9-419 R. MTI, Budapest, 1964.

[108] Korvin-Kroukovsky, B. V.: Some Similarity Relationships for Towing Tank Models Used in Combined Ship Structural and Hydrodynamic Experiments. Int. Shipbuilding Progress, March, Vol. 9, No. 91, 1962.

[109] Köröndi, L.–Szittner, A.: A hídszerkezetek dinamikus méretezésének néhány problémája (Some Problems of Dynamic Dimensioning of Bridge Structures).

[110] Köröndi, L.–Szittner, A.: Az Erzsébet-hídon végzett dinamikus próbaterhelés eredményei (Results of the Dynamic Load Test of the Elizabeth Bridge). Mélyépítéstudományi Szemle, 2, 1968.

[111] Kristóf, L.–Szatmári, I.–Szittner, A.: A Kiskörei Vízlépcső szegmensgát megtámasztásának modellkísérleti vizsgálata (Model Investigation of the Support Pivot of the Segment Gate of the Kisköre Barrage). Mélyépítéstudományi Szemle, February, 1961.

[112] Kristóf, L.–Szittner, A.: Dynamische Untersuchungen an der Tisza-Strassenbrücke bei Tiszafüred. Periodica Polytechnica Vol. 13, No. 3–4. Budapest, 1969.

[113] Kristóf, L.–Szittner, A.: Dinamikus vizsgálatok a tiszafüredi közúti Tisza-hídon (Dynamic Investigations on the Tiszafüred Bridge on the Tisza), Mélyépítéstudományi Szemle, 5, 1970.

114] Krummet, R.: Untersuchung von Schwingungserscheinungen am unteren Verschluss zweier hintereinander angeordneter Tiefschützen. MAN Forschungsheft, Nr. 11. 1963–64.

[115] Krummet, R.: Schwingungsverhalten von Verschlussorganen im Stahlwasserbau bei grossen Druckhöhen, insbesondere von Tiefschützen. Forschung im Ingenieurwesen, Bd. 31, Nr. 5. 1965.

[116] Laird, A. D. K.: Water Forces on Flexible Oscillating Cylinders. Proc. ASCE WW3, August, 1962.

[117] Landweber, L.: Dimensional Analysis of Ship Vibration. Manuscript, September, 1962.

[118] Landweber, L.: Vibration of a Flexible Cylinder in a Fluid. J. Ship Research, Sept. Vol. 11, No. 3, 1967.

[119] Landweber, L.–de Macagno, M. C.: Added Mass of Two-Dimensional Forms Oscillating in a Free Surface. J. Ship Research, November, 1957.

[120] Landweber, L.–Macagno, M.: Added Masses of Two-Dimensional Forms by Conformal Mapping. J. Ship Research, June, 1967.

[121] Lange, F.: On the Problem of Apparent Mass. IAHR Symposium, Stockholm, 1970.

[122] Lean, G. H.: The Vibration of a Coffer Dam Wall Near the Axis of a Jet. XIth IAHR Congress, Leningrad, 1965.

[123] Lecher, W. A.: Cavitation Observations and Noise Measurements as a Means of Investigating the Trailing-Edge Vibrations of Turbine Blades. Xth IAHR Congress. London, 1963.

[124] Levin, A.: Nécessité de la prise en considération de la condition de Reech-Froude dans la similitude de phénomènes hydroélastiques turbulents. Journal of Hydraulic Research, Vol. 9, No. 3, 1971.

[124a] Levin, L.: Phénomènes vibratoires observés sur des vannes-segment déversantes. La Houille Blanche, 6, 1971.

[125] Levin, L.–Meaulle, A.: Étude de l'amortissement hydraulique de la vibration d'une baguette en régime turbulent. XIVth IAHR Congress, Paris, 1971.

[126] Levis, E. V.: Ship Model Tests to Determine Bending Moments in Waves, SNAME, Vol. 62, 1954.

[126a] Лятхер, В. М.—Складнев, М. Ф.—Шейнин, И. С.: Исследования в области динамической гидроупругости гидротехнических сооружений (Studies in the Field of Dynamic Hydroelasticity of Hydraulic Structures). Гидротехническое строительство 8, 1971.

[127] Ljisenko, P. E.: On Hydroelastic Correlations between Different Forms of Oscillations of Plate in the Flow Boundary Resulting from Non-Uniform Distribution. XIVth IAHR Congress, Paris, 1971.

[128] Люстерник, Л. А.—Болинского, В. А.: Расчет физических полей методами моделирования (Calculation of Physical Fields by the Method of Modelling). Машиностроение, Москва, 1968.

[129] Locher, F. A.: Some Aspects of Flow-Induced Vibrations of Hydraulic Control Gates. Doctoral thesis, Graduate College of the University of Iowa. February, 1969.

[130] Ludvig, Gy.: Lengésvizsgálatok (Vibration Studies). Lecture Note No. 66-2559 T.MTI, Budapest, 1966.

[131] Macagno, E. O.: Masa adicional y red potencial. Seminario Latinoamericano de Hidráulica y Mecánica de Fluidos, Santiago de Chile, 1962.

[132] Major, A.: Vibration Analysis and Design of Foundations for Machines and Turbines. Akadémiai Kiadó, Budapest, 1962.

[133] Marris, J. W.: A Review on Vortex Streets, Periodic Wakes, and Induced Vibration Phenomena. J. Basic Engineering (ASME). June, 1964.

[134] McGoldrick, R. T.: Ship Vibration. Report 1451, December, 1960. Department of the Navy. David Taylor Model Basin.

[135] McLachlan, N. W.: Theory of Vibrations. Dover Publications, Inc. New York, 1961.

[136] McLean, W. J.–Laird, A. D. K.–Brewer, J. W.: Behavior of a Flexibly Supported Cylinder in a Fluid Stream. Report No. HPS-64-3. Nov., 1964. Institute of Engineering Research, Univ. of Calif. Berkeley, Calif.

[137] Meier-Windhorst, A.: Flatterschwingungen von Zylindern im gleichmässigen Flüssigkeitsstrom, München, Technische Hochschule, Hydraulische Inst. Mitt., Vol. 9, 1939.

[138] Meier-Windhorst, A.: Flutter Vibrations of Cylinders in a Uniform Flow. David Taylor Model Basin, Translation 333, July, 1966.

[139] Mikhailov, A. V.–Rosanov, N. P.: General Report on Subject 4- Hydroelasticity, XIth IAHR Congress, Leningrad, 1965.

[140] Morrow, D. J.–Schutzenhofer, L. A.–Reed, T. G.–Shish, C. C.: Experimental Investigation of Effects of Unsteady Flows on a Submerged Cylinder. XIVth IAHR Congress, Paris, 1971.

[141] Murray, R. I.–Simmons, W. P.: Hydraulic Downpull Forces on Large Gates. A Water Resources Technical Publication. Research Report No. 4. United States Dept. of the Interior, Bureau of Reclamation.

[142] Murphy, T. E.: Model and Prototype Observations of Gate Oscillations, Xth IAHR Congress, London, 1963.

[143] Muttnyánszky, Á.: Szilárdságtan (Strength of Materials). Tankönyvkiadó, Budapest, 1957.

[144] Naudascher, E.: On the Role of Eddies in Flow-Induced Vibrations. Xth IAHR Congress, London, 1963.

[145] Naudascher, E.: Hydrodynamic Forces on Non-Steady Conditions (General report). XIVth IAHR Congress, Paris, 1971.

[146] Naudascher, E.: Effect of Interacting Periodic Wakes on the Vibration of Multiple-Leaf Gates. XIth IAHR Congress, Leningrad, 1965.

[147] Naudascher, E.: Vibration of Gates during Overflow and Underflow. American Society of Civil Engineers, Transactions, Vol. 127, Part I, 1962.

[148] Naudascher, E.: From Flow Instability to Flow-Induced Excitation. Journal of the Hydraulics Division (ASCE) July, 1972.

[148a] Naudascher, E.: Entwurfskriterien für schwingungssichere Talsperrenverschlüsse. Wasserwirtschaft, 1–2, 1972.

[148b] Naudascher, E.: Discussion. Stoplog Closure–Model Prototype Correlation. Journal of the Hydraulics Division, Vol. 100, HY2, February, 1974.

[148c] Naudascher, E.–Locher, F. A.: Flow-Induced Forces on Protruding Walls. Journal of the Hydraulics Division, ASCE, Vol. 100, HY2, February, 1974.

[148d] Nandascher, E.: Flow-Induced Vibrations — A Unified Approach. XVIIth IAHR Congress, Baden-Baden, 1977.

[149] Назаров, А. Г.–Шагинян, С. Г.–Шагинян, С. А.–Севоян, А. А.:: Моделирование строительных конструкций на сейсмические воздействия (Modelling of Structures for Seismic Effects) Изд. АН Армянский ССР, Ереван, 1968.

[150] Nelson, M. E.–Johnson, H. J.–Fidelman, S.: Lifting Forces on Lock Valves, VIIIth IAHR Congress, Montreal, 1959.

[151] Németh, E.: Hidromechanika (Hydromechanics).Tankönyvkiadó, Budapest, 1963.

[152] Novak, M.–Davenport, A. G.: Aeroelastic Instability of Prisms in Turbulent Flow. Journal of Engineering Mechanics Division. Proc. ASCE, EM 1, February, 1970.

[153] Ochi, K.: Model Experiments on Submarine Chaser in Irregular Waves. Japanese original: 1957. English translation: Davidson Laboratory, SIT, Note 499, Sept, 1958.

[154] Owais, T. M.–Toebes, G. H.: The Measurements of Energy Transfer between Oscillating Bodies and Surrounding Flow by Means of Analog Correlation. NSF GK-00414, Hydromechanics Laboratory, Purdue University, Technical Report No. 18, October, 1968.

[155] Partenscky, H. W.–Abhimanyn Swain: Theoretical Study on Flap Gate Oscillation. XIVth IAHR Congress, Paris, 1971.

[156] Perkins, J. A.: Model Investigations of the Vibration of a Vertical-Lift Sluice Gate. Xth IAHR Congress, London, 1963.

[157] Petrikat, K.: New Developments on Hydraulic Sector Gates. VIIIth IAHR Congress, Montreal, 1959.

[158] Petrikat, K.: Schwingungsuntersuchungen an Stahlwasserbauten. Der Stahlbau, 24, 1955.

[159] Petrikat, K.: Die schwingungsanfachenden Kräfte im Wehrbau. MAN-Forschungsheft, 4, 1953.

[159a] Petrikat, K.: Bestimmung der schwingungserregenden Vertikalkräfte an Sohldichtungen von Hubschützen und Segmentwehrverschlüssen. Mitteilungen des Instituts für Wasserbau, Stuttgart, Nr. 21, 1972.

[159b] Prosser, M. J.: Seaforth Works–Model Study of the Sector Gates. Flow Model Investigations for Hydraulic Structures. Research Results. The British Hydromechanics Research Association (BHRA), Cranfield, 1971.

[160] Protos, A.–Goldschmidt, V. W.–Toebes, G. H.: Hydroelastic Forces on Bluff Cylinders. Journal of Basic Engineering (ASME) 68-Fe-12, 1968.

[161] Pyber, L.: Model Investigation into the Stop-Log Closure of the Nagymaros Barrage. Brno Symposium, 1967.

[162] Pyber, L.: Vibration Investigations (Diploma Work, Manuscript), Delft, 1968.

[163] Pyber, L.: Hidraulikai rezgéstani jelenségek kismintavizsgálata. Irodalomfeltárás. Összefoglaló jelentés (Model Investigation of Hydroelastic Phenomena. Closing Report). Budapest, 1968. (Manuscript at the VITUKI Library.)

[163a] Raudkivi, A. J.–Small, A. F.: Hydroelastic Excitation of Cylinders. Journal of Hydraulic Research, 12, No. 1. 1974.

[164] Ridjanović, M.: Drag Coefficients of Flat Plates Oscillating Normally to their Planes. Schiffstechnik, Bd. 9. Heft 45, 1962.

[165] Robson, J. D.: An Introduction to Random Vibration. Edinburgh University Press, Edinburgh, 1963.

[166] Rouse, G. C.–Bouwkamp, J. G.: Vibration Studies of Monticello Dam. A Water Resources Technical Publication. Research Report No. 9. U.S. Dept. of Interior, Bureau of Reclamation, Denver–Washington, 1967.

[166a] Rueff, H.: Die Messung von instationären Kräften auf Tiefschützenmodelle in einem Kavitations-Versuchsstand. Mitteilungen des Instituts für Wasserbau, Stuttgart, Nr. 21, 1972.

[167] Russel, R. C. H.: Hydrodynamic Forces in Free Surface Flow (General report). XIVth IAHR Congress, Paris, 1971.

[168] Russo, G. A.–Sheinin, I. S.: On Investigations of the Dynamics of Hydraulic Structures. XIth IAHR Congress, Leningrad, 1965.

[169] Rusz, E. (Mrs.): A nagymarosi hajózsilip töltő- és ürítőberendezésének kismintavizsgálata. Összefoglaló jelentés. (Model Investigation of the Filling and Emptying System of the Nagymaros Navigation Lock. Closing Report.) Budapest, 1955. (Manuscript at the VITUKI Library.)

[170] Sagar, B. T. A.–Tullis, J. P.: Problems with Recent High-Head Gate Installations. IAHR Symposium, Stockholm, 1970.

[171] Sato, M.: Model Experiments on the Longitudinal Strength of Ships Running Among Waves. Japanese original: 1951. English translation: Davidson Laboratory, SIT, Report No. 614. December, 1956.

[171a] Schmidgall, T.: Spillway Gate Vibrations on Arkansas River Dams. Journal of the Hydraulic Division. ASCE. Vol. 98, HY1, January, 1972.

[172] Schoemaker, H. J.: Dynamics of a Sluice Gate and a Movable Weir Subject to Forces Exerted by Waves and to Vibration. Survey of Model Investigations. VIIIth IAHR Congress, Montreal, 1959.

[173] Schwartz, H. I.: A Study of the Trajectory of a Two-Dimensional Nappe of Projected Liquid. The Civil Engineer in South Africa Vol. 5, No. 1, January, 1963.

[174] Schwartz, H. I.: Edgetones and Nappe Oscillation. The Journal of Acoustical Society of America, Vol. 39, No. 3, 1966.

[175] Schwartz, H. I.–Nutt, L. P.: Projected Nappes Subject to Transverse Pressure. Journal of the Hydraulics Division (ASCE), July, 1963.

[176] Schwartz, H. I.: Nappe Oscillation. Journal of the Hydraulics Division (ASCE), November, 1964.

[177] Scruton, C.–Lambourne, N. C.: Similarity Requirements for Flutter Model Testing. Manual on Aeroelasticity. North Atlantic Treaty Organisation Advisory Group for Aeronautical Research and Development, 1959( ?).

[177a] Sharp, J. J.: Basic Applications of Similitude Theory. Water and Water Engineering, September, 1973.

[178] Shaw, T. L.: Wake Dynamics of Two-dimensional Structures in Confined Flows. XIVth IAHR Congress, Paris, 1971.

[179] Sheinin, J. S.–Zhulyova, J. S.: Hydrodynamic Forces Due to Nonstationary Oscillations of Cylindrical Shells in a Fluid Medium with Deformations of the Cross-Section Taken into Account. XIVth IAHR Congress, Paris, 1971.

[180] Silbersdorff, L.: Lengéstan (Vibration Theory). University lecture note No. J7-138. R. Tankönyvkiadó, Budapest, 1965.

[181] Skoglund, V. J.: Similitude. Theory and Applications. International Textbook Company, Scranton, Pennsylvania, 1967.

[182] Spillway and Outlet Works Ft. Randall Dam, Missouri River, Tech. Report No. 2-528. U. S. Army Corps of Engrs. Waterways Experiment Station, Vicksburg, Miss., October, 1959.

[183] Steinman, D. B.: Problems of Aerodynamic and Hydrodynamic Stability. Proc. of the Third Hydraulics Conference. Bulletin 31, Univ. of Iowa Studies in Engineering. 1947.

[184] Stollmayer, Á.: Rezgésjelenségek a vízépítési műtárgyakon (Vibration Phenomena on Hydraulic Structures). Hidrológiai Közlöny, 4, 1958.

[185] Sutton, M.: Pump Scale Laws as Affected by Individual Component Losses. Symposium on Model Testing of Hydraulic Machinery and Associated Structures. Cranfield, 1968.

[186] Седов, Л. И.: Методы подобия и размерность в механике (The Methods of Similarity and Dimensional Analysis in Mechanics). 5th edition. Изд. Наука, Москва, 1965.

[186a] Swain, A.–Tzou, K.–Palmer, H.: Discussion. Flow-Induced Forces on Protruding Walls. Journal of Hydraulics Division. Vol. 101, No. HY7, July, 1975.

[186b] Swedish State Power Board, the Hydraulic Laboratory Älvkarleby: Niger Dam Project–Kainji Development. The Use of Stop-Logs for Spillway Closure at Stage III Diversion. Report on Hydraulic Model Tests, 1970.

[187] Szeloch, L.: The Influence of Flow upon Vibrations of Vertical-Lift Gate Model. XIth IAHR Congress, Leningrad, 1965.

[188] Szittner, A.: Kísérleti feszültséganalízis I–II. (Experimental Stress Analysis I–II). Lecture notes Nos. J9-375 and J9-417. MTI, Budapest, 1964–65.

[189] Szittner, A.: Témapályázati bírálat, Haszpra Ottó „A nagymarosi duzzasztómű egy betétgerendájának rezgéstani kismintavizsgálata" c. összefoglaló jelentéséről (Scientific Competition Criticism on the Closing Report Titled "Hydroelastic Model Investigation of a Stop-Log of the Nagymaros Barrage" by O. Haszpra). Manuscript, Budapest, 1966.

[190] Szűcs, E.: A hasonlóságelmélet alapjai (Fundamentals of Similitude Theory). Műszaki Könyvkiadó, Budapest, 1967.

[191] Szűcs, E.: A hasonlóságelmélet alkalmazása. Modellkísérletek (Application of Similitude Theory, Model Experiments). Műszaki Könyvkiadó, Budapest, 1969.

[192] Szűcs, E.: Similarity and Models. Elsevier, Amsterdam, 1978.

[192a] Szűcs, E.: A hasonlósági módszer és építőipari alkalmazásai. Doktori értekezés (The Method of Similitude and Its Applications for the Building Industry. Doctoral Dissertation). Manuscript. Budapest, 1971.

[193] Thomas, A. R.–Lean, G. H.: The Vibration of a Submerged Wall Exposed to a Jet. Xth IAHR Congress. London, 1963.

[194] Thomas, W.: Hydraulic Performance of 96-Inch Regulating Gates in Closed Conduits. VIIIth IAHR Congress, Montreal, 1959.

[195] Thomson, W. T.: Vibration Theory and Applications. Prentice-Hall, Englewood Cliffs, N. J., 1965.

[196] Toebes, G. H.: Fluidelasticity, XIth IAHR Congress, Leningrad, 1965.

[197] Toebes, G .H.: The Frequency of Oscillatory Forces Acting on Bluff Cylinders in Constricted Passages. XIVth IAHR Congress, Paris, 1971.

[198] Toebes, G. H.: The Unsteady Flow and Wake Near an Oscillating Cylinder. Journal of Basic Engineering (ASME), 68-WA-23, 1968.

[199] Toebes, G. H.: Fluidelasticity. Lecture note of Purdue University, Lafayette, Ind. 1968.

[200] Toebes, G. H.: Hydrodynamic Forces on Boundaries Due to Unsteady Flow (General Report). XIVth IAHR Congress, Paris, 1971.

[201] Toebes, G. H.: Hydroelastic Forces on Hydraulic Structures Due to Turbulent Wake Flows. IXth IAHR Congress, Dubrovnik, 1961.

[202] Toebes, G. H.: Flow-Induced Structural Vibrations. Journal of the Engineering Mechanics Division (ASCE), December, 1965.

[203] Toebes, H.: Fluidelastic Features of Flow Around Cylinders. International Research Seminar: Wind Effects on Buildings and Structures, September, 1967. Ottawa, Canada.

[204] Toebes, G. H.–Ramamurthy, A. S.: Fluidelastic Forces on Circular Cylinders. Journal of the Engineering Mechanics Division (ASCE), EM6, December, 1967.

[205] Toebes, G. H.–Eagleson, P. S.: Hydroelastic Vibrations of Flat Plates Related to Trailing Edge Geometry. Journal of Basic Engineering (ASME), 61-Hyd-16, 1961.

[206] Turner, J. J.–Warters, R. L.–Eagleson, P. S.: The Effect of Transverse body Vibration on the Spanwise Correlation of Instantaneous Wake Structure for Flat Plates. Hydrodynamics Laboratory Report No. 81. Dept. of Civil Engineering. MIT, Cambridge, USA, 1965.

[207] Ujihara, B. H.–Oder, H. S.–Harris, L. A.: Hydroelastic Analysis of a Circular Cylinder. SD 68–996. Space Division North American Rockwell Corporation, December, 1968.

[208] Uppal, H.: Vibration Problems in Hydraulic Structures. Discussion, Proc. ASCE, Journal of the Hydraulics Division, November, 1961.

[209] Venkataraman, C. P.–Golé, C. V.: Hydrodynamic Forces Caused by Unsteady Slot Flow on Vertical Leaf Gates. XIVth IAHR Congress, Paris, 1971.

[210] Vértes, Gy.: Rezgéstan (Vibration Theory). Lecture note No. J9-522/a, MTI, Budapest, 1965.

[211] Vlcek, M.: Forces Acting on a Floating Body Elastically Fastened in an Inclined Tank. XIth IAHR Congress, Leningrad, 1965.

[212] Walter, J.: Hydroelastic Vibrations of High Head Gates. XIth IAHR Congress, Leningrad, 1965.

[213] Walter, J.–Ganapathy, K. T.–Thomas, B.: Vibration Characteristics of Sluice Gates. Xth IAHR Congress, London, 1963.

[214] Wasserman, L. S.–Mykytow, W. J.: Model Construction. Manual on Aero-elasticity. NATO Advisory Group for Aeronautical Research and Development. 1959(?).

[215] Webber, N. B.: Fluid Mechanics for Civil Engineers, E. & F. N. Spon Ltd. London, 1965.

[216] Weber–White–Manning: Physics for Science and Engineering, McGraw-Hill, New York, Toronto, London, 1957.

[217] Wu Jin: Froude-Number Scaling of Wind-Stress Coefficients. A Correlation for Wind Stresses Determined at All Fetches. Hydronautics, Incorporated. Technical Report 231–23, 1968.

[218] Zaky, H.–Sauvage de St.–Mark, M. G.: Experimental Results of a Free Jet Downstream of a Gate with Various Partial Openings. VIIIth IAHR Congress, Montreal, 1959.